ANNUAL REVIEW OF GERONTOLOGY AND GERIATRICS

VOLUME 28, 2008

Annual Review of Gerontology and Geriatrics

Gerontological and Geriatric Education

VOLUME 28, 2008

Volume Editors

HARVEY L. STERNS, PhD
MARIE A. BERNARD, MD

Series Editor

K. WARNER SCHAIE

SPRINGER PUBLISHING COMPANY

New York

Springer Publishing Company, LLC
11 West 42nd Street
New York, NY 10036
www.springerpub.com

Acquisitions Editor: Sheri W. Sussman
Production Editor: Julia Rosen
Composition: Apex CoVantage, LLC

09 10 11 12 / 5 4 3 2 1

ISBN 978–0–8261–0099–3
ISSN 0198–8794

Printed in the United States of America by Bang Printing.

Contents

Section I: Evolution of Gerontology and Geriatrics Education

Section III: Approaches to Gerontology Education and Application

About the Volume Editors

Harvey L. Sterns, PhD, is professor of psychology and director and senior fellow of the Institute for Life-Span Development and Gerontology at The University of Akron. He is research professor of gerontology at the Northeastern Ohio Universities College of Medicine and Pharmacy. He is a faculty member in both the Psychology of Adult Development and Aging and Industrial/Organizational Psychology graduate programs, and chairs the specialization in Industrial Gerontological Psychology. He has published extensively on cognitive intervention, work and retirement, career development, training and retraining, and self-management of career and retirement. He is a licensed psychologist in Ohio and is a fellow of the Gerontological Society of America, American Psychological Association, Association for Psychological Science, and Association for Gerontology in Higher Education. He has served as president of Division 20 Adult Development and Aging of the American Psychological Association, Association for Gerontology in Higher Education, and Sigma Phi Omega National Academic and Professional Society in Gerontology. He is a past board of trustees member of the American Society on Aging. He has served or serves on the editorial boards of *Psychology of Aging, Experimental Aging Research, The Gerontologist, Research on Aging, and Women and Aging.*

Marie A. Bernard, MD, is the Donald W. Reynolds Chair in Geriatric Medicine, and professor and chairman of the Donald W. Reynolds Department of Geriatrics at University of Oklahoma. She is also associate chief of staff for geriatrics and extended care at the Oklahoma City Veterans Affairs Medical Center. She is chairman of the board of the Association of Directors of Geriatric Academic Programs (ADGAP) and immediate past president of the Association for Gerontology in Higher Education.

Dr. Bernard's research interests include nutrition and function in aging populations, with particular emphasis on ethnic minorities. She serves or has served on the following committees and boards: Institute of Medicine Committee, The Future Health Care Workforce for Older Americans; chair, National Research Advisory Council, Department of Veterans Affairs; board of directors member, American Geriatrics Society, Alliance for Aging Research, and International Longevity Center; editorial board member, *Journal of Gerontology Medical Sciences* and *The Gerontologist.* She is past chair of the Clinical Medicine Section of the Gerontological Society of America and past president of ADGAP. She has also served on the National Advisory Council for the National Institute of Aging, having chaired the Minority Task Force during her tenure.

Contributors

Edward Ansello, PhD, Director, Virginia Center on Aging, Medical College of Virginia Campus, Virginia Commonwealth University, Richmond, VA

Robert Applebaum, PhD, Professor, Department of Sociology and Gerontology and Director of the Ohio Long-Term Care Research Project, Scripps Gerontology Center, Miami University, Oxford, Ohio

Robert H. Binstock, PhD, Professor, Division of Health Services Research School of Medicine, Case Western Reserve University, Cleveland, OH

Kenneth Ferraro, Professor of Sociology, Director, Center on Aging in the Life Course, Purdue University, West Lafayette, Indiana

Joseph H. Flaherty, MD, Geriatric Research Education and Clinical Center (GRECC), VA Medical Center and Division of Geriatric Medicine, Saint Louis University, School of Medicine, St. Louis, Missouri

Julie K. Gammack, MD, Division of Geriatric Medicine, Saint Louis University, School of Medicine, St. Louis, Missouri

Judith L. Howe, PhD, Associate Professor, Brookdale Department of Geriatrics and Adult Development, Mount Sinai School of Medicine, Associate Director, Education and Evaluation, VISN 3 Geriatric Research Education and Clinical Center (GRECC) at the James J. Peters VA, and Director, Consortium of NY Geriatric Education Centers, New York, NY

Marshall B. Kapp, JD, MPH, Garwin Distinguished Professor of Law and Medicine, Southern Illinois University, School of Law and School of Medicine, Carbondale, IL

Suzanne R. Kunkel, PhD, Director and Professor, Scripps Gerontology Center, Department of Sociology and Gerontology, Miami University, Oxford, OH

Jessie Leek, PhD (cand.), Doctoral Student, Department of Sociology and Gerontology, Miami University, Oxford, Ohio

Ronald J. Manheimer, PhD, Executive Director, North Carolina Center for Creative Retirement, The University of North Carolina at Asheville, Asheville, North Carolina

Melen R. McBride, PhD, RN, GSAF, Associate Director, Emeritus, Stanford Geriatric Education Center, Stanford University, School of Medicine, Stanford, California

Jennifer Mendez, PhD, Director of Longitudinal Curricular Theme, School of Medicine, Wayne State University, Detroit, MI

John E. Morley, MB, BCh, Geriatric Research Education and Clinical Center (GRECC), VA Medical Center and Division of Geriatric Medicine, Saint Louis University, School of Medicine, St. Louis, Missouri

Miguel A. Paniagua, MD, Division of Geriatric Medicine, Saint Louis University, School of Medicine, St. Louis, Missouri

Anthony A. Sterns, PhD, Director of Research Creative Action, LLC, Akron, OH

Nina Tumosa, PhD, GRECC, VA Medical Center and Division of Geriatric Medicine, Saint Louis University, School of Medicine, St. Louis, Missouri

Donna M. Weinreich, PhD, Assistant Professor, School of Social Work, Western Michigan University, Kalamazoo, MI

Gwen Yeo, PhD, AGSF, Codirector, Stanford Geriatric Education Center, Stanford University, School of Medicine, Stanford, California

Forthcoming

ANNUAL REVIEW OF GERONTOLOGY AND GERIATRICS, 2009

Volume 29: Health Inequalities: Life Course Perspectives on Late Life Outcomes

Series Editor: K. Warner Schaie, PhD
Volume Editors: Toni Antonucci, PhD,
and James S. Jackson, PhD

Previous Volumes in the Series

Acknowledgments

This volume required very special effort on the part of each contributor. Everyone is extremely involved in education, research, and practice in one form or another. We are truly grateful for their willingness to join us in this enterprise.

Harvey Sterns wishes to acknowledge the 37 years of support that he has received from colleagues at the University of Akron in developing courses and programs in gerontology. Special thanks to Cecile Becker and Karen Aiken, graduate students, for helping with this volume.

Marie Bernard wants to acknowledge the faculty and staff of the Donald W. Reynolds Department of Geriatric Medicine at University of Oklahoma. Without their support, she would not have been able to serve as a coeditor of this volume.

Both of us would like to acknowledge the 28 years of the *Annual Review of Gerontology and Geriatrics* and the contributions of previous series editors and volume editors to this important resource. We want to give a special thanks to Sheri Sussman, senior vice president, editorial, and Deborah Gissinger, assistant editor of Springer Publishing Company, for their support and help in making this volume a reality.

Harvey L. Sterns, PhD, Akron, Ohio
Marie A. Bernard, MD, Oklahoma City, Oklahoma

SECTION I

EVOLUTION OF GERONTOLOGY AND GERIATRICS EDUCATION

This section provides an overview of gerontology and geriatrics education, starting from a past perspective, and projecting into the future, both for the United States and internationally. The section is led by a chapter titled "The Evolution of Gerontology Education Over Three Decades: Reflections and Prospects," by Harvey L. Sterns of The University of Akron and Kenneth F. Ferraro of Purdue University. They trace the development of gerontology education in the United States and discuss current and future challenges for growth and development of gerontology as a discipline and the relationship to other disciplines.

The next chapter is by Marie A. Bernard of University of Oklahoma and is titled "Workforce Needs in the Future: The Institute of Medicine 2008 Report—Retooling for an Aging America." Dr. Bernard provides a summary of the background considerations and recommendations from the Institute of Medicine committee report that was released April 14, 2008. The committee made recommendations for enhancement of training of all health care professionals in geriatrics, increased recruitment and retention of geriatrics specialists, and reconfiguration of health care provision to optimize the care provided to older individuals. This chapter details those considerations.

The third chapter is by John E. Morley, Miguel A. Paniagua, Joseph H. Flaherty, Julie K. Gammack, and Nina Tumosa at St. Louis University and is titled "The Challenges to the Continued Health of Geriatrics in the United States." Dr. Morley et al. provide a summary of the history of the development of geriatrics in the United States and an accounting of current geriatrics workforce availability. They discuss the challenges to the maintenance of the geriatrics workforce and make predictions for the future of geriatrics in the United States.

Suzanne R. Kunkel of Miami University concludes this section with a description of gerontology education across the globe. Her chapter, titled "Global Aging and Gerontology Education: The International Mandate," discusses global aging rates. She then provides details regarding gerontology education in the United States, Israel, Japan, the European Union, and Kenya. She argues for the need for cross-national perspectives within gerontology education and presents methods by which this education can be provided.

CHAPTER 1

The Evolution of Gerontology Education Over Three Decades

Reflections and Prospects

Harvey L. Sterns and Kenneth F. Ferraro

Gerontology is, in many ways, a young scientific field of study, and systematic discussion of how to educate gerontologists is an even more recent phenomenon. As gerontology scholars have sought to define the field, there is the related question of how to educate students interested in the study of aging. More specific questions abound: What curriculum is deemed essential? Is there a paradigm for the field that can be cogently expressed to students? How should gerontology education programs be structured?

These and other questions received systematic attention in the United States during the 1970s. Sensing the magnitude of the task, a multidisciplinary collection of gerontology scholars spearheaded the creation of the Association for Gerontology in Higher Education (AGHE) in 1974. And the energy of AGHE's early years resulted in a spurt of reports and books addressing the aforementioned questions (e.g., Seltzer, Sterns, & Hickey, 1978; Sterns, Ansello, Sprouse, & Layfield-Faux, 1979). Although it is not our aim to comprehensively answer those seminal questions in this chapter, we believe there is value in (a) reviewing some of the major changes during the past 30 years and (b) identifying salient issues that have yet to be resolved. Indeed, in some ways, it has been argued that many of the debates have not advanced much at all (Ferraro, 2006). In other ways, the changes have been dramatic.

DOI: 10.1891/0198-8794.28.3

AUSPICIOUS BEGINNINGS: GERONTOLOGY
AS A GROWTH INDUSTRY

Over 30 years ago, a number of important vectors came together to produce an increased interest—and excitement—in the field of aging as well as new expectations for postsecondary education related to an aging society (Sterns, 1978). First was the growth in the older segment of the population—prompting some to call for 20/20 vision when the Baby Boom moves en mass into retirement (Ferraro & Sterns, 1990). Second was the increased interest in research in life span/life cycle development and gerontology. Third was the increased funding from federal, state, and local agencies for education and training in the field of aging. Fourth was the dramatic increase in agencies and institutions providing direct services to older people—a consequence of the Great Society initiatives of the 1960s. These included federal agencies, state units on aging, area agencies on aging, local government offices, planning agencies, multipurpose senior centers, older adult services agencies, preretirement preparation programs, older adult housing and planned retirement communities, long-term care facilities, nutrition programs, and numerous other paid and volunteer organizations.

In the midst of these trends, the environment seemed ripe for gerontology as a growth industry. Especially because of the increase in service agencies and programs, it seemed only logical that there was a need for workers and administrators with training in gerontology. This perceived need was anticipated at the paraprofessional, administrative, technical, and professional levels. Thus, many also felt an immediate need to augment the training of in-service personnel and to include gerontology education in the preservice preparation of students in existing degree programs. How could workers appropriately organize and deliver services to older adults without some type of education in gerontology? Gerontology educators felt that the future was bright for program expansion to adequately address the human resource expectations. Many identified a growing need for college-level researchers and teachers to carry out the training and education of potential and current workers in the field.

The enthusiasm of the 1970s was tempered by a variety of concerns, including the appearance of so-called instant gerontologists, quality academic programs, the need to focus on research to provide a better scientific base for the field, funding for research and program development, and even the need for quality textbooks, handbooks, and other educational materials. Building on the earlier volumes, a more formal treatment of gerontology education emerged with Peterson and Bolton's (1980) book *Gerontology Instruction in Higher Education*. This book captured many of the core issues with which gerontology programs struggled, and many of these issues remain eerily similar to contemporary debates.

Educational institutions had increased opportunities to offer workshops and seminars, noncredit courses, and credit courses for both preservice and in-service students. In a number of states, training officers from state units on aging helped to stimulate educational opportunities using state and local Title III and IV-A funds. Some educational institutions found this to be an exciting challenge and a natural extension of ongoing programs, while some had to be dragged in, and still other institutions failed to become involved at all.

The responses of particular educational institutions at the time were determined by interest, history, and faculty strength. There were a number of mature gerontology programs in this country, some going back to right after World War II. The vast majority of educational institutions, however, found themselves responding to these new demands during the 1970s.

A relatively small number of faculty members trained in established programs in life span/life cycle development, gerontology, or geriatric care had the opportunity to implement development of gerontology education on their campuses. Many of these faculty had been hired in traditional departmental settings and had begun to develop relevant course work, degree programs, and in some cases university-wide programs. Other faculty decided to retool themselves, perhaps with a postdoctoral fellowship, so that they were better prepared to stimulate educational and research initiatives on their campuses. Federal training funds from the Administration on Aging, Title IV-A and IV-C were available to support the development of new higher education programs. Some states like Ohio developed cooperative state-wide collaborations between educational institutions and the Area Agencies on Aging. Ohio also allocated funding through the Ohio Board of Regents to create Offices of Geriatric Medicine and Gerontology in all seven medical schools in Ohio during the late 1970s.

At the national level, the AGHE came into being during 1974 and held its first national meeting in 1975. The national meeting has become a major forum for gerontology education and program development (Binstock, 2007). Literally hundreds of educational programs were birthed at institutions, including community colleges and research-intensive universities. For the most part, gerontology was delivered via a minor, certificate, or specialization.

The excitement and growth of this early period of development continued into the 1980s but was interrupted during the Reagan Administration, which eventually cut training funds allocated under Title IV. Although Administration on Aging funding for gerontology education was sharply reduced, there has been funding from the National Institute on Aging (NIA) for specific pre- and postdoctoral training. Since 1985 the Bureau of Health Professions also funded Geriatric Education Centers (see chapter 11, this volume), albeit with the unfortunate loss of funding for 1 year and the resulting interruption even though funds have since been made available.

One of the great success stories of gerontology education is that through the commitment of colleges and universities using both internal and external funding there are now over 770 programs representing over 350 institutions in gerontology and geriatrics (AGHE, 2008). These include certificate programs; minors and specializations; associate, bachelor, and master's degrees; fellowships, post-docs, and residencies; and six PhD programs in gerontology. Gerontology emerged as a science with a substantial educational network for the next generation of scholars interested in aging (Achenbaum, 1995; Wilmoth & Ferraro, 2007).

The intellectual capital for gerontology also increased during the time that gerontology programs proliferated on campuses. For instance, 11 gerontology journals were created during the 1970s, and 31 gerontology journals were added during the 1980s (Ferraro, 2007). Discussions of a paradigm for gerontology emerged in the 1990s, prompting consideration of a gerontological imagination for scholars regardless of their field of study (Ferraro, 1990). Gerontology penetrated the core disciplines, transforming them to attend to major themes in aging research (e.g., skepticism about aging effects, modifiability of aging, ageism). At the same time, there have been efforts to create a more integrated approach to gerontology education, and many scholars favor a new discipline for the study of aging.

All in all, the future for gerontology education remained bright, despite some challenges to institutional development of gerontology programs. The net result, as Ferraro (2006) described, was that "gerontology at most colleges and universities is by and large a nice supplement to existing programs. Many universities are trying to do more with less, and gerontology often finds itself in this position" (p. 573). It could be argued that many successful academic programs remain fragile, suggesting the need for sober attention to local institutional histories when seeking to develop gerontology programs. Beyond the structural issues of gerontology's location in the university, there have been important debates regarding the need for gerontologists.

ESSENTIAL OR ENDEARING: WHO NEEDS A GERONTOLOGIST?

It is widely acknowledged that gerontology, the scientific study of aging, is a field of inquiry that draws from many disciplines including biology, psychology, sociology, political science, history, anthropology, economics, humanities, and ethics (Bass & Ferraro, 2000). The definition of a gerontologist is someone who is committed to the *science of aging*. At the same time, we expect that scientific discoveries will be translated in such a way as to optimize the benefit to humanity. For gerontology, this leads to a focus on application: "To be an applied gerontologist is to be an interventionist" (Sterns & Camp, 1998, p. 177). Those individuals who specialize in the application of medical knowledge to the care of older people and related research are geriatricians. Geriatric medicine has become well established throughout the world but is still coming of age in the United States (see chapters 2 and 3 in this volume).

In many discussions of professional education in the United States, there has been a focus on whether we need specialists to *meet the needs of older adults* or whether all members of a profession should be well-trained in aging. In the latter case, specialization is not required. There is little debate that there should be basic knowledge in gerontology and geriatrics for all professionals serving older adults. However, the last three decades have taught us that at least at this point in time that we also need to have specialists in gerontology, persons who are uniquely qualified to understand and advocate for high-quality services for older adults. All of the professional groups since the 1940s have developed special sections, divisions, interest groups, and so forth in gerontology and/or geriatrics, and many of these sections are promoting specialty guidelines and qualifications.

The question for our time is *whether our society needs gerontologists*. In some ways, educating a gerontologist is a logical, perhaps essential, response to the trends that we are observing: both the aging of the population and the growth in life expectancy. At the same time, the core disciplines and professions are incorporating many of the discoveries and extant knowledge into their programs of study, thereby muting the need for distinctively trained gerontologists. Especially for service professions, such as social work and nursing, that require certification, gerontology seems to be having a difficult time being treated as a legitimate sister occupation. Indeed, few positions in today's society are described for gerontologists. In many situations, it seems that gerontologists have to use other credentials to gain access to positions dedicated to serving older people.

A major point of discussion 30 years ago by leaders in gerontology education was that the field of gerontology needed to be able to develop on each campus with an appreciation of the history and strength of individual institutions. Mildred Seltzer, Harold Johnson, and Hiram Friedsam, among others, were also concerned that gerontology would become highly proscriptive as had happened with social work and nursing. Although certification was eschewed, the Foundations for Gerontology Education project provided an important step in the development of the field with its emphasis on a core curriculum (Johnson et al., 1980). The consensus at the time was that the core curriculum was decidedly multidisciplinary, and that no single academic discipline, profession, or department had a lock on the field of gerontology. Indeed, this is one point that has changed very little in nearly three decades (Ferraro, 2006). The eloquent discussion of gerontology as an emerging discipline by Alkema and Alley (2006) supports the importance of gerontology further developing into an *integrative* discipline.

We believe that there is a need for a full spectrum of professionals specializing in aging *within* the widely established disciplines. At the same time, there is value in promoting the development of *gerontology as a discipline*. Degree programs in gerontology need to be supported as a key part of the long-term development of the field of aging. However, we have witnessed an unpleasant side effect where people with degrees in gerontology are not recognizing well-trained individuals with certificates, minors, and other specialized qualifications as gerontologists. At this point in time, the field needs to offer mutual support to multiple paths to being a gerontologist.

The demographic imperative of an aging world needs to be embraced, and action is needed. Instead, what we have seen is immobilization. The core demands for well-trained individuals to provide direct services, planning, and administration by Area Agencies on Aging and State Units on Aging must be met. Low levels of funding have many agencies providing the most basic of services. We are not able to apply a great deal of gerontological knowledge that we have today because of limited resources. There has also been continued resistance to develop career ladders and to integrate paraprofessional education into our higher education system.

There remains a need for traditional degrees such as BSN, MSN, BSW, and MSW to fill positions in service to older adults. Programs that add gerontology with certificates and specializations can meet much of the need for trained individuals. At the same time, we need to promote the highest level of new developments in the field. New degrees in gerontology will require new professional categories and licensure. The developments here have been discussed for many years, but many gerontologists remain concerned about the push for licensure and certification.

Other important innovations include the creation of new areas such as bringing gerontology into colleges of business or administration. The AGHE Task Force on Business and Aging has promoted ways to implement aging in business courses. Courses in finance, marketing, consumer behavior, and human resource management need to address aging issues. One example of this approach is the new MBA/MSG at the University of North Carolina at Greensboro.

With the proliferation of graduate degrees in gerontology, we see a key distinction between master's and doctoral degrees. Although many see master's degrees in gerontology as a step toward a PhD in gerontology, we believe that master's degrees in gerontology represent an excellent way to address the *service* needs of elders. In many ways, master's degrees in gerontology may be less than optimal for students seeking a PhD because most doctoral programs are heavily developed from the core disciplines. Thus, students with gerontology MS degrees may be disadvantaged when applying for PhD programs in the core disciplines. By contrast, we propose greater attention to a MSG as a terminal degree for service professionals, parallel to the MSW and the MPH. The master's degree would be focused on the practice of gerontology (i.e., intervention), perhaps with optional specialties such as long-term care administration, financial planning, and wellness.

The conventional path to doctoral education in gerontology is to study in a more established discipline, whether anthropology or pharmacy administration, and integrate gerontology into that plan of study. Some of the new doctoral programs are basically structured in an inside out fashion. Instead of gerontology being the specialty as in the most traditional PhD programs, many gerontology PhD programs make gerontology the major, with a minor that is often a major field of study (e.g., nutrition). The packaging of such credentials remains a matter of considerable debate. Some programs offer gerontology doctoral credentials that minimize the risk of employment uncertainty for students. One example is offered by Purdue University in Indiana, which pairs gerontology with an established discipline in a dual-title PhD program.

GERONTOLOGY LEADERSHIP IN THE MAKING

As we think of the evolution of gerontology education, it may also be useful to conclude by briefly considering how the field is changing from a life span perspective. One can also view gerontology's evolution through the lens of cohort flow.

In the science of aging, we recognize normative history-graded influences on a particular cohort, a group of people who share a similar experience at the same time (in this case developing gerontology programs). For instance, consider the faculty who were trained in the late 1960s and early 1970s. These scholars experienced a period of rapid growth and support for gerontology program development and the availability of considerable government funding for gerontology *education* programs. Some of these faculty also played an important role in training the new group of individuals to provide direct service via community agencies.

Nonnormative life events are unusual events that may occur at an atypical time in development. Such events can be positive or negative. One example is the major change in funding for academic gerontology during the Reagan Administration when funding went from over 20 million to 5 million at a critical time in program development in the early 1980s. Another example would be the recent defunding (and, a year later, refunding) of Geriatric Education Centers.

In terms of cohort flow, time is running out for the first generation of gerontologists who received fellowships from either the first wave of National Institute of Child and Human Development or from the Administration on Aging. These faculty members who embraced university leadership have created and implemented programs in gerontology in one form or another on their campuses. Their contributions have helped to shape the present, but their legacy will become clearer with time. Whatever the case, the real issue is how the torch will be passed to the next generation.

When one considers how these general trends map onto specific campuses, which have their own developmental histories, one can see that there is a wide diversity of outcomes. Some programs are very successful, some are moderately successful, some are barely surviving, and others have been discontinued. This has occurred at a time when the need for personnel in the field of aging remains critical.

Gerontology educators and researchers are divided by a number of approaches to gerontology education. These differences go back decades ago when the first certificates in gerontology where given with traditional disciplinary degrees. There have been significant advances within the traditional disciplines with a focus on issues of aging and the emergence of courses and major areas of research. Master's and doctoral programs in gerontology emerged starting in the 1970s and 1980s, respectively. Although many of these programs are flourishing, it could be argued that "the field has reached its current state through substantial struggles. In truth, the field's remarkable gains remain quite fragile" (Binstock, 2008, p. 3).

Binstock (2008) further summarized the situation by noting that these struggles are played out in the lives of persons interested in gerontology.

> In the early 1960's, fewer than 10 college and university programs focused on aging, although a growing number of individuals were becoming interested in the subject. Today the Association for Gerontology in Higher Education lists an impressive 772 programs in gerontology and geriatrics.

These range from certificate programs and fellowships to master's and Ph.D. programs.... Funding for many of the programs is tenuous and remains an ongoing concern for education leaders in gerontology.... Many researchers have found that focusing on aging has posed difficulties for their career advancement and success. (p. 4)

Indeed, the same concerns led Pelham (2008) to describe the fragile status of gerontology as follows.

Many gerontology programs are ... comparatively small programs administered and taught by few, often part-time faculty.... Although the offering of gerontology coursework in other disciplines is valuable and the participation of interdisciplinary faculty is welcome, helpful and enriching to the field, the long term health of a gerontology program ultimately requires discipline-based resources and recognition. (p. 3)

Gerontology is endearing to an aging society, but it is not in many ways deemed essential. We believe that we must first make a stronger case for the need for gerontologists, and we hold that it is important to distinguish roles for those educated at the master's and doctoral levels. For professionals serving older adults directly or administering services, we recommend that the master's programs be charged with educating the next generation of gerontologists. For leadership in gerontology education, we believe the diversity of approaches will ultimately serve the field well as it slowly evolves toward a new discipline.

REFERENCES

Achenbaum, W. A. (1995). *Crossing frontiers: Gerontology emerges as a science.* Cambridge: Cambridge University Press.

AGHE, Association for Gerontology in Higher Education. (2008). *AGHE program database.* Washington, DC.

Alkema, G. E., & Alley, D. E. (2006). Gerontology's future: An integrative model for disciplinary advancement. *The Gerontologist, 46,* 574–582.

Bass, S. A., & Ferraro, K. F. (2000). Gerontology education in transition: Considering disciplinary and paradigmatic evolution. *Gerontologist, 40,* 97–107.

Binstock, R. H. (2007). Gerontology in higher education: An autobiographical memoir. *Journal of Aging, Humanities, and the Arts, 1,* 245–258.

Binstock, R. H. (2008, March–April). Gerontology: A fragile field. *Aging Today,* 3–4.

Ferraro, K. F. (1990). The gerontological imagination. In K. F. Ferraro (Ed.), *Gerontology: Perspectives and issues* (pp. 3–18). New York: Springer Publishing.

Ferraro, K. F. (2006). Imagining the disciplinary advancement of gerontology: Whither the tipping point? *The Gerontologist, 46,* 571–573.

Ferraro, K. F. (2007). The evolution of gerontology as a scientific field of inquiry. In J. M. Wilmoth & K. F. Ferraro (Eds.), *Gerontology: Perspectives and issues* (3rd ed., pp. 13–34). New York: Springer Publishing.

Ferraro, K. F., & Sterns, H. L. (1990). Epilogue: "2020 vision" and beyond. In K. F. Ferraro (Ed.), *Gerontology: Perspectives and issues* (pp. 357–360). New York: Springer Publishing.

Johnson, H. R., Britton, J. H., Lang, C. A., Seltzer, M. M., Stanford, E. P., Yancik, R., et al. (1980). Foundations for gerontological education. *The Gerontologist, 20*(3, Pt. 2), 1–61.

Pelham, A. (2008, March–April). Can academic gerontology keep from becoming irrelevant? *Aging Today,* 3–4.

Peterson, D. A., & Bolton, C. R. (1980). *Gerontology instruction in higher education.* New York: Springer Publishing.

Seltzer, M. M., Sterns, H. L., & Hickey, T. (1978). *Gerontology in higher education: Perspectives and issues.* Belmont, CA: Wadsworth Publishing Company.

Sterns, H. L. (1978). First steps in program development: Developmental tasks. In M. M. Seltzer, H. L. Sterns, & T. Hickey (Eds.), *Gerontology in higher education: Perspectives and issues* (pp. 104–109). Belmont, CA: Wadsworth Publishing.

Sterns, H. L., Ansello, E. F., Sprouse, B. M., & Layfield-Faux, R. (1979). *Gerontology in higher education: Developing institutional and community strength.* Belmont, CA: Wadsworth Publishing.

Sterns, H. L., & Camp, C. J. (1998) Applied gerontology. *Applied Psychology: An International Review, 17,* 175–198.

Wilmoth, J. M., & Ferraro, K. F. (2007). The fountain of gerontological discovery. In J. M. Wilmoth & K. F. Ferraro (Eds.), *Gerontology: Perspectives and issues* (3rd ed., pp. 3–12). New York: Springer Publishing.

CHAPTER 2

Workforce Needs in the Future

The Institute of Medicine 2008 Report—
Retooling for an Aging America

Marie A. Bernard

WORKFORCE NEEDS IN THE FUTURE

The Institute of Medicine (IOM) issued a report on April 14, 2008, titled *Retooling for an Aging America,* addressing the geriatrics workforce needs of the future (IOM, Committee on the Future Health Care Workforce for Older Americans, 2008). The committee that developed the report was tasked with determining (a) the future health status and utilization of services by older Americans, (b) the best use of the health care workforce, given projections for future health and utilization, (c) the education and training, recruitment, and retention of health care professionals that will be needed, and (d) what needs to be improved in public programs to support the care of older Americans. The committee was convened with support from a number of private foundations (see Table 2.1), and had representatives from a variety of areas of expertise, ranging from geriatric medicine to health economics and social policy (see Table 2.2). This chapter reviews the findings and recommendations within the report.

Retooling for an Aging America is best summarized by considering, as the committee did, the current state of health and workforce availability for aged Americans. From this examination came a number of recommendations and some suggestions for what should be done in the future. Thus this chapter addresses why the report is important, its findings and recommendations, as well as suggestions for the future.

13
DOI: 10.1891/0198-8794.28.13

TABLE 2.1

Foundations Supporting the IOM Report

AARP
Archstone Foundation
Atlantic Philanthropies
California Endowment
Commonwealth Fund
Fan Fox and Leslie R. Samuels Foundation
John A. Hartford Foundation
Josiah Macy, Jr., Foundation
Retirement Research Foundation
Robert Wood Johnson Foundation

TABLE 2.2

IOM Committee Members

- **John W. Rowe** (chair) Columbia University
- **Paula G. Allen-Meares** University of Michigan
- **Stuart H. Altman** Brandeis University
- **Marie A. Bernard** University of Oklahoma
- **David Blumenthal** Massachusetts General Hospital
- **Susan A. Chapman** University of California, San Francisco
- **Terry T. Fulmer** New York University
- **Tamara B. Harris** National Institute on Aging
- **Miriam A. Mobley Smith** Chicago State University
- **Carol Raphael** Visiting Nurse Service of New York
- **David B. Reuben** University of California, Los Angeles
- **Charles F. Reynolds III** University of Pittsburgh
- **Joseph E. Scherger** University of California, San Diego
- **Paul C. Tang** Palo Alto Medical Foundation
- **Joshua M. Wiener** RTI International

WHY IS RETOOLING FOR AN AGING AMERICA IMPORTANT?

Future Increases in the Population

The 65-year-old and over population has been increasing since the middle of the 20th century. Currently those 85 years old and older are the most rapidly expanding portion of the population (Department of Health and Human

Services [DHHS] & Centers for Disease Control and Prevention [CDC], 2007). By 2030, the date for which the IOM report makes projections, 20% of the U.S. population is anticipated to be 65 years and older (IOM, 2008). This is a population that is anticipated to have more diverse needs than did prior generations, with increased numbers of ethnic and other minorities.

Older Persons Use More Services

Current populations of elders have a variety of accumulated illnesses, with coronary artery disease, hypertension, cancer, diabetes, emphysema, and Alzheimer's disease being among the top causes of death (DHHS & CDC, 2007). Older individuals are more likely to have multiple chronic illnesses, including heart disease, hypertension, arthritis, stroke, emphysema, and diabetes (DHHS & CDC, 2007). Projections for the future health of the aged population can range from a similar constellation of illnesses to improved health as a result of better access to health care and better health habits. Alternatively, future older generations may have worse health than the current cohort, because of the obesity epidemic (Olshansky et al., 2005). Currently, as a result of multiple illnesses, older individuals utilize significant health care resources. Annual drug costs for individuals 65 and over were $2,107 in 2004; 365 of every 1,000 Medicare enrollees were hospitalized in 2005; and health care costs in 2004 ranged from approximately $7,000 per Medicare enrollee 65–74 years old to $22,000 per Medicare enrollee 85 and over (Federal Interagency Forum on Aging-Related Statistics, 2008).

Current Care Is Not Optimal

Current care is not optimal, in part because of lack of training of health professionals regarding the needs of older individuals. Eighty percent of deaths occur over age 65. Although almost all medical schools and 62% of pharmacy schools provide exposure to geriatrics content (IOM, 2008), the adequacy of that exposure is questionable. As reported by the Association of Directors of Geriatric Academic Programs (ADGAP), 23% of medical schools require a geriatrics clerkship and 48% integrate geriatrics into a required clinical rotation (Warshaw, Bragg, & Shaull, 2002). However, in 34% of medical schools, curriculum depended on faculty interest. In 17% of schools there was some exposure; however, there were no objectives (Warshaw et al., 2002). Primary care residents completing their training often feel unprepared to care for the elderly or those residing in nursing homes (Blumenthal, Gokhale, Campbell, & Weissman, 2001). Residents in specialties such as gynecology, general surgery, orthopedics, and anesthesiology feel unprepared for interdisciplinary interactions that are essential for the optimal care of frail elders (Blumenthal et al., 2001).

Current care is also not optimal because of problems with the care provision system. There is little guidance on effective interventions specific to the elderly. In those cases where guidance is available, the proportion of recommended care that is received declines with age. Models of care that have been shown to be effective and efficient are not implemented widely. There is also lack of payment for interdisciplinary care, care coordination, patient education, and geriatric expertise, all of which have been shown to be effective and efficient in the care of the elderly (IOM, 2008).

Inadequate Workforce
There are not a sufficient number of geriatrics specialists. In 2008, there are approximately 7,100 board-certified geriatricians, with that number declining as a result of physicians retiring and/or choosing not to recertify. There are approximately 1,600 board-certified geriatric psychiatrists, with similar problems with physicians not recertifying (ADGAP, 2005). It is noteworthy that in 2000 there were approximately 9,000 board-certified geriatricians. This number has declined in spite of increased numbers of training slots in geriatric medicine and geriatric psychiatry (ADGAP, 2005). In fact, in September 2007 the national survey of graduate medical education programs reported a 14% decrease in the number of first-year geriatric medicine fellows from 2005–2006 to 2006–2007, with only 34 advanced fellows (i.e., beyond the first year) during the 2006–2007 academic year (Brotherton & Etzel, 2007). Both geriatric medicine and psychiatry hit their peak certification rates when it was feasible for physicians to take the certifying exam based on years of practice experience. Once certification was only feasible through a fellowship, the number of board-certified geriatricians and geriatric psychiatrists declined (ADGAP, 2005).

The challenge of specialists in the care of the elderly is seen in multiple other disciplines, including nursing, dentistry, pharmacy, and social work, to name a few. Although elderly patients are seen in 23% of office visits and 47% of hospital visits by advanced practice registered nurses (APRNs), only about 2.6% of APRNs are certified in geriatrics, with only 300 geriatric APRN graduates annually (IOM, 2008). Less than 1% of registered nurses (RNs) are certified in geriatrics (IOM, 2008). Almost one-third (29%) of baccalaureate programs have a certified faculty member. Approximately one-third of baccalaureate programs require exposure to geriatrics (IOM, 2008). The number of geriatrics faculty and training requirements in geriatrics are unknown for associate degree programs, one of the major sources of nurses who provide direct care to the elderly.

In dentistry geriatrics is not recognized as a specialty for certification. As of the IOM report there were 13 programs for academic geriatric dentistry, with no residencies specific to geriatrics. Geriatrics is not explicitly tested on board examinations (IOM, 2008).

In pharmacy less than 1% of pharmacists are certified in geriatrics. Out of a total of 351 residency programs in pharmacy, there are only 10 residency programs in geriatric pharmacy, with one fellowship position in Alzheimer's disease (IOM, 2008).

In social work, 40% of schools lack faculty in aging. Eighty percent of bachelors programs have no coursework in aging. Less than one-third (29%) of masters (MSW) programs offer an aging focus. A point of significant concern is that in the 1980s, almost half of MSW programs offered specialization in aging (IOM, 2008).

There are challenges with recruiting geriatrics specialists in the various health disciplines for several reasons. These include negative stereotypes of older adults, lower incomes, the high cost of training, and lack of opportunity for advanced training. Studies have recurrently demonstrated that young health professionals have negative views and attitudes towards aging (Bernard, McAuley, Belzer, & Neal, 2003). It has been shown that geriatric-trained physicians have a diminished return on the investment of geriatric fellowship training as compared to the compensation that they could receive by going directly into practice (Weeks & Wallace, 2004). Geriatric medicine physicians receive, on average, $165,000 in annual compensation, which is equivalent to that of a general internist (IOM, 2008). Specialists in gastroenterology, anesthesiology, radiology, and obstetrics and gynecology receive an average compensation of approximately $250,000–$425,000 annually (Woo, 2006). Although this degree of compensation appears generous, the average indebtedness of medical school graduates in 2002 was $86,870 (Rosenblatt & Andrilla, 2005). Additionally, it has been found that there is an inverse relationship between a commitment to a primary care career, such as geriatrics, and medical school indebtedness, with the most marked association being with indebtedness of $150,000 or greater (Rosenblatt & Andrilla, 2005). In every field examined, as outlined previously, opportunities for advanced training are limited by lack of faculty and (with the exception of geriatric medicine) training programs (IOM, 2008).

The workforce is particularly challenged at the level of the direct-care worker, where there is inadequate retention of staff. There is reportedly an average 71% turnover of nurse aides in direct care, with some institutions exceeding 100% turnover (IOM, 2008). Approximately $4.1 billion is spent each year in retraining staff, because of high levels of turnover. Much of this can be attributed to the low levels of pay received by direct-care workers. Personal and home-care aides earn on average $8.54 per hour, as contrasted with food counter attendants who earn an average of $7.76. Direct-care workers are more likely to lack health insurance and use food stamps (IOM, 2008). Should the food service industry begin to provide health insurance, the direct-care worker field would be devastated.

There is insufficient training of the general health care workforce in caring for the elderly. Despite promising changes occurring among medical schools, professionals generally receive little training in the common problems of older adults. Direct-care workers are particularly deficient in training regarding the care of the elderly. Federal training minimums have not changed in 20 years and may be lower than that for dog groomers, cosmetologists, and crossing guards (IOM, 2008). In many cases that training does not require specific content regarding the elderly, nor demonstration of competency. The segment of the population that spends the most time with frail elders, informal caregivers such as family and friends, generally receive little training.

WHAT WERE THE RECOMMENDATIONS OF THE IOM COMMITTEE?

Given this background, the IOM panel developed recommendations in three areas—(a) enhancement of geriatric competence of the general workforce in common problems, (b) increasing recruitment and retention of geriatric specialists and caregivers, and (c) implementation of innovative models of care. Table 2.3 provides a concise listing of the IOM recommendations.

Enhancement of Geriatric Competence of General Workforce in Common Problems

The panel chose to make recommendations related to health care professionals (doctors, nurses, social workers, pharmacists, etc.), direct-care workers (nurse aides, home health aides, personal and home care aides), and informal caregivers (families and friends).

Health Professionals

The panel recommended that all licensure, certification, and maintenance of certification for health care professionals include demonstration of competence in the care of older adults as a criterion. Currently, the vast majority of older

TABLE 2.3
IOM Recommendations

Enhancing Competence

Recommendation 4.2

All licensure, certification, and maintenance of certification for health care professionals should include demonstration of competence in the care of older adults as a criterion.

Recommendation 4.1

Hospitals should encourage the training of residents in all settings where older adults receive care, including nursing homes, assisted-living facilities, and patients' homes.

Recommendation 5.1

States and the federal government should increase minimum training standards for all direct-care workers.

Federal requirements for the minimum training of certified nurse assistants and home health aides should be raised to at least 120 hours, including demonstration of competence in the care of older adults as a criterion for certification.

States should also establish minimum training requirements for personal care aides.

Recommendation 6.2

Public, private, and community organizations should provide funding and ensure that adequate training opportunities are available in the community for informal caregivers.

Increasing Recruitment and Retention of Geriatric Specialists and Caregivers

Recommendation 4.3

Public and private payers should provide financial incentives to increase the number of geriatric specialists in all health professions.

   a. Enhancement of reimbursement for clinical services delivered to older adults by practitioners with geriatric certification.
   b. Enhancement of the Geriatric Academic Career Award (GACA) program to support junior geriatrics faculty in other health professions in addition to medicine.
   c. Loan forgiveness, scholarships, and direct financial incentives for professionals who become geriatric specialists, National Geriatrics Service Corps.

Recommendation 5.2

State Medicaid programs should increase pay and fringe benefits for direct-care workers.

Implementing Innovative Models of Care

Recommendation 3.1

Promote the dissemination of those models of care for older adults that have been shown to be effective and efficient.

(continued)

TABLE 2.3
(continued)

Recommendation 3.2

Increase support for research and demonstration programs.
- Promote development of new models
- Promote effective use of the workforce

Recommendation 3.3

Expand the roles of individuals beyond the traditional scope of practice, such as through job delegation.
- Development of an evidence base
- Measurement of additional competence
- Greater professional recognition and salary

Recommendation 6.1

Support technological advancements that could enhance an individual's capacity to provide care for older adults.
- ADL technologies
- Health information technologies, including remote technologies

Monitoring

Recommendation 1.1

Annual report from the Bureau of Health Professions to monitor the progress made in addressing the crisis in supply of the health care workforce for older adults.

Note. Recommendations are numbered according to the chapter in which they are found in the full report.

individuals are seen by non–geriatrics-trained individuals (Xakellis, 2004), as there are small numbers of geriatrics experts in the health professions. Requiring demonstrated competence in the care of the elderly would assure that all health professionals have a basic level of skills and knowledge, which would allow the utilization of geriatrics specialists for the more challenging problems of the elderly. The panel also recommended that hospitals encourage the training of resident physicians in all settings where older adults receive care, including nursing homes, assisted-living facilities, and patients' homes. By that means, whether the physician was an orthopedist, gynecologist, or primary care provider, the physician would have familiarity with the continuum of care available for the care of the elderly, and would be more likely to appropriately refer patients for that care.

Direct-Care Workers

The panel had several recommendations related to direct-care workers and informal caregivers. They recommended that states and the federal government increase minimum training standards for all direct-care workers. They further recommended that federal minimum training requirements for certified nurse assistants and home health aides be raised to at least 120 hours and include demonstration of competence in the care of older adults as a criterion for certification. Currently, there are some training programs with content related to the care of the elderly, but this is not uniformly found; nor is there routine expectation that competence be demonstrated (IOM, 2008). Finally, they recommended that states establish minimum training requirements for personal care aides.

Informal Caregivers

The panel recommended that public, private, and community organizations provide funding and ensure that adequate training opportunities are available in the community for informal caregivers. It was recommended that this training be provided in easily consumable form and be available when the caregiver needed it, recognizing that need is not necessarily realized until the caregiver is in a crisis situation.

Increasing Recruitment and Retention of Geriatric Specialists and Caregivers

Recommendations by the panel regarding recruitment and retention of geriatric specialists focused on professionals and direct-care workers. To enhance the number of professionals who were geriatrics specialists, the committee recommended that public and private payers provide financial incentives to increase the number of geriatric specialists in all health professions. The committee also recommended enhancement of reimbursement for clinical services delivered to older adults by practitioners with geriatric certification, in order to overcome the current adverse return on investment for geriatrics training (Goodman & Fisher, 2008; Weeks & Wallace, 2004). The panel also recommended enhancement of the Geriatric Academic Career Award (GACA) program. This program, sponsored by the Health Resources Services Administration (HRSA), has supported junior geriatrics faculty in medicine within the last decade. In order to develop a sufficient number of faculty with geriatrics expertise who are able to teach other health professionals, the panel recommended expansion of the GACA program to cover additional health professions. The panel also recommended the development of loan forgiveness, scholarships, and direct financial incentives for professionals who become geriatrics specialists. Loan forgiveness has shown promise to be effective in the recruitment of geriatrics specialists in South Carolina (Hirth, Eleazer, & Dever-Bumba, 2008). Finally, the panel recommended the development of a National Geriatrics Service Corps, modeled after the Public Health Service Corps. Such an innovation could conceivably help with the deployment of geriatrics-trained professionals in areas of highest need.

As noted previously in this chapter, direct-care workers receive marginal pay. Nineteen percent of female direct-care workers have incomes below the poverty level, and about 25% of all direct-care workers have no health insurance coverage (IOM, 2008). Thus the panel recommended that state Medicaid programs increase pay and fringe benefits for direct-care workers.

Implementation of Innovative Models of Care

The IOM committee carefully considered the things that would be necessary to redesign public programs to support more effective and efficient care for the elderly. In this consideration, they concluded that there was a need to disseminate known models that have been shown to be effective, discover additional newer models, expand individual roles of health professionals, and improve the capacity and safety of the elderly care recipient.

In redesigning models of care, several principles were considered. First, it was noted that the health needs of the older population need to be addressed comprehensively. A single-disease approach to a frail older individual with multiple illnesses could benefit the disease of focus but lead to adverse outcomes with other diseases. Additionally, without a comprehensive approach to the care of the elderly, disease could be modified but undesirable outcomes could occur related to function and quality of life. Second, the committee required that services be provided efficiently, with a focus on cost-effectiveness. Finally, ideal models of care would include older persons and their caregivers as active partners in their care. An extensive literature review was conducted with these principles in mind, leading to a number of effective models of care being identified. Common features of these models included interdisciplinary team care, care management, chronic disease self-management, caregiver education and support, pharmaceutical management, proactive rehabilitation, preventive home visits, and transitional care. Examples include the Grace and PACE programs (Counsell et al., 2007; Wolff & Boult, 2005).

Based on the literature review, the panel developed a number of recommendations for implementation of innovative models of care. First, the panel recommended promotion of the dissemination of those models of care for older adults that have been shown to be effective and efficient. More than 100 such models were identified. Much of the benefit of these models was the removal of traditional funding barriers, such as the separation of Medicare and Medicaid funds. Additionally, these models took advantage of the common features listed above, such as interdisciplinary team care, care management, and so forth.

Second, the panel recommended increased support for research and demonstration programs to promote development of new models and to promote effective use of the workforce. For instance, some models, such as the PACE program, have been found to be more effective in areas with a high concentration of elders and health professionals (Wolff & Boult, 2005). Effective models of care for areas with long distances separating elders and care providers, and for ethnic and other minority populations, need further development.

The committee also recommended the expansion of the roles of various members of the health care team beyond the traditional scope of practice, such as through job delegation. For instance, the impact of a nurse, dentist, or physician could be increased by delegation of some of their duties to a nurse aide, dental technician, or physician extender. Delegation of job duties to other professionals would ultimately lead to career ladders for the advancement of direct-care workers. However, in order for this to be effective, it will be necessary to develop an evidence base for job delegation, a means to measure additional competence, and opportunities for greater professional recognition and salary.

Finally, the committee recommended the support of technological advancements that could enhance an individual's capacity to provide care for older adults. There were a number of activities of daily living technologies that were presented during testimony to the committee that could assist the older individual and the caregiver in providing care. Additionally, health information technologies, including remote technologies, could facilitate an older individual remaining within the home rather than requiring institutionalization.

Monitoring

The committee's overarching recommendation to facilitate implementation and monitoring of the recommendations was for HRSA's Bureau of Health Professions to develop an annual report monitoring the progress made in addressing the crisis in supply of the health care workforce for older adults. This report would be provided to the Secretary of the DHHS, to facilitate further modification in workforce training and deployment as needed.

WHERE DO WE GO FROM HERE?

In order for this report to be effective, it requires support and dissemination by all individuals interested in the health care needs of our aging society. There clearly are cost implications to the recommendations. The scope of the committee's charge did not include a careful calculation of those costs. However, the committee noted that continuing in the current path cannot be fiscally sustained and needs modification.

In summary, this IOM panel found that the health care workforce for our aging society is insufficient for needs that can be anticipated by 2030. In order to meet those needs, all providers (including family and friends) need to have core competencies in caring for older persons. These competencies need to be instilled during general training and reinforced lifelong for health care providers. Training in these competencies needs to be provided when needed for informal caregivers.

REFERENCES

Association of Directors of Geriatric Academic Programs. (2005). Longitudinal study of training and practice in geriatric medicine. *Training and Practice Update, 3*(1). Retrieved July 24, 2008, from http://www.adgapstudy.uc.edu/Files/ADGAP%20Training%20and%20Practice%20Update%203_1.pdf

Bernard, M., McAuley, W. J., Belzer, J. A., & Neal, K. S. (2003). An evaluation of a low-intensity intervention to introduce medical students to healthy older people. *Journal of the American Geriatrics Society, 51*(3), 419–423.

Blumenthal, D. M., Gokhale, E., Campbell, G., & Weissman, J. S. (2001). Preparedness for clinical practice of graduating residents at academic health centers. *Journal of the American Medical Association, 286,* 1027–1034.

Brotherton, S. E., & Etzel, S. I. (2007). Graduate medical education, 2006–2007. *Journal of the American Medical Association, 298*(9), 1081–1096.

Counsell, S. R., Callahan, C. M., Clark, D. O., Tu, W., Buttar, A. B., Stump, T. E., et al. (2007). Geriatric care management for low-income seniors: A randomized controlled trial. *Journal of the American Medical Association, 298*(22), 2623–2633.

Department of Health and Human Services & Centers for Disease Control and Prevention. (2007). *The state of aging and health in America 2007 report.* Retrieved July 24, 2008, from http://www.cdc.gov/aging/saha.htm

Federal Interagency Forum on Aging-Related Statistics. (2008). *Older Americans 2008: Key indicators of well-being.* Retrieved July 24, 2008, from http://agingstats.gov/agingstatsdotnet/main_site/default.aspx

Goodman, D. C., & Fisher, E. S. (2008). Physician workforce crisis? Wrong diagnosis, wrong prescription. *New England Journal of Medicine, 358,* 1658–1661.

Hirth, V. A., Eleazer, G. P., & Dever-Bumba, M. (2008). A step toward solving the geriatrician shortage. *American Journal of Medicine, 121*(3), 247–251.

Institute of Medicine, Committee on the Future Health Care Workforce for Older Americans. (2008). *Retooling for an aging America: Building the healthcare workforce.* Washington, DC: National Academy Press.

Olshansky, S. J., Passaro, D. J., Hershow, R. C., Layden, J., Carnes, B. A., Brody, J., et al. (2005). A potential decline in life expectancy in the United States in the 21st century. *New England Journal of Medicine, 352,* 1138–1145.

Rosenblatt, R.A., & Andrilla, C.H. (2005). The impact of U.S. medical students' debt on their choice of primary care careers: An analysis of data from the 2002 medical school graduation questionnaire. *Academic Medicine, 80*(9), 815–819.

Warshaw, G. A., Bragg, E. J., & Shaull, R. W. (2002).*The Association of Directors of Geriatric Academic Programs (ADGAP) longitudinal study of training and practice in geriatric medicine. Geriatric medicine training and practice in the United States at the beginning of the 21st century.* New York: ADGAP.

Weeks, W. B., & Wallace, A. E. (2004). Return on educational investment in geriatrics training. *Journal of the American Geriatrics Society, 52*(11), 1940–1945.

Wolff, J. L., & Boult, C. (2005). Moving beyond round pegs and square holes: Restructuring Medicare to improve chronic care. *Annals of Internal Medicine, 143*(6), 439–445.

Woo, B. (2006). Primary care—the best job in medicine? *New England Journal of Medicine, 355*(9), 864–866.

Xakellis, G. C. (2004). Who provides care to Medicare beneficiaries and what settings do they use? *Journal of the American Board of Family Practice, 17*(5), 384–387.

CHAPTER 3

The Challenges to the Continued Health of Geriatrics in the United States

John E. Morley, Miguel A. Paniagua, Joseph H. Flaherty,
Julie K. Gammack, and Nina Tumosa

The illiterate of the 21st century will not be those who cannot read and write, but those who cannot learn, unlearn and relearn.

—Alvin Toffler (1980)

This chapter represents a historical summary and description of the current circumstances of geriatrics. It also discusses the projections of the future workforce in geriatrics.

Since ancient times there has been an understanding that older persons differ physiologically from younger persons and are affected differently by disease processes. This has led to numerous treatises over the centuries highlighting the different physical, psychological, and social needs of older persons. The knowledge base in these texts has eventually led to the foundation of the modern specialty of geriatrics (Morley, 2004).

The heyday of geriatrics began at the turn of the 20th century when Ignatz Leo Nascher coined the term geriatrics in his text titled *Longevity and Rejuvenescence* (Nascher, 1909). He felt that geriatrics should be considered a distinct medical discipline. The term *geriatrics* was derived from *geronte*, a group of men over 60 years of age who ran the legislative council (*gerocina*) of ancient Athens. Multiple national programs in geriatrics have since been created. These program include:

- In the 1940s, under the leadership of Malford W. Thewlis and E. Vincent Cowdry, the American Geriatrics Society (1942) was formed.
- The Gerontological Society (now the Gerontological Society of America) were formed in 1945.
- The modern research-focused development of geriatrics in the United States began with the formation of the Unit on Aging and the gerontology branch and section on aging as part of the National Institutes of Health programs in the late 1940s and early 1950s (Morley & Gammack, 2006).
- The first fellowship in geriatric medicine was offered by Dr. Leslie Libow at Mount Sinai School of Medicine in 1966. He also led the development of academic nursing home programs.
- The National Institutes of Aging was formed in 1976 under the leadership of Robert Butler.
- The first professorship in geriatric medicine was granted at Cornell University in 1977.
- The American Medical Directors Association was formed in 1978 under the leadership of Herman Gruber, Dr. William Dodd, and Dr. James Pattee.
- Also in 1978, the American Association of Geriatric Psychiatry was founded.
- The greatest impetus for modern clinical geriatrics and geriatric education strongly grounded in a research background was directly due to the development of the VA Geriatric Research Education and Clinical Centers (GRECCs) in 1975. The GRECCs began offering geriatric medicine fellowship training opportunities in 1978.
- Mount Sinai School of Medicine established the first department of geriatrics in 1982. By 2001 there were three departments of geriatric medicine in allopathic medical schools and three in osteopathic schools. At the present time there are eight allopathic medicine departments of geriatric medicine (Mt. Sinai School of Medicine, University of Arkansas, University of Oklahoma, University of Florida College of Medicine, East Tennessee State University, Florida State University, University of Hawaii, Wright State University in Dayton) and four osteopathic medicine departments (Nova Southeastern University College of Osteopathic Medicine, Philadelphia College of Osteopathic Medicine, Ohio University College of Osteopathic Medicine, and Edward Via Virginia College of Osteopathic Medicine in Blacksburg). The most common geriatric academic structure is a division or a subsection of a division within the 125 allopathic medical schools and the 20 osteopathic medical schools.

The growth of geriatrics has been strongly influenced by fiscal support from a number of philanthropic agencies. The first of these was the Josiah Macy, Jr. Foundation (http://www.josiahmacyfoundation.org) in the 1930s and 1940s. Since the early 1980s, the John A. Hartford Foundation (http://www.jhartfound.org) has supported geriatrics by the funding of Centers of Excellence and by providing direct support for medical students doing research in geriatrics. They have also funded interdisciplinary care curriculum development with a focus on nursing and social workers. They have provided funding to increase awareness of geriatrics in a variety of medical and surgical specialties and to develop medical student education. More recently the Donald W. Reynolds Foundation (http://www.dwreynolds.org/) has provided large amounts of fiscal support to many medical schools to enhance their geriatrics programs. The Brookdale Foundation (http://www.brookdalefoundation.org), originally endowed by the Schwarz Family, has provided important support for the development of future leaders in geriatrics. The Alzheimer's Association (http://www.alz.org/), founded in 1980, has played a major role in increasing awareness of dementias and in funding research in this area.

Another major funder of the development of geriatrics in the United States has been the Geriatric Education Centers (GECs). These programs, funded by the Health Resources and Services Administration, fund interdisciplinary training using a train-the-trainers approach and also develop new geriatrics curricula for students. They have provided important continuing medical education as well as faculty support at medical schools.

Besides its intramural program and its funding of research grants, the National Institutes of Aging has played an important role in the development of geriatrics through its centers—Claude D. Pepper Older American Independence Centers, Alzheimer Centers, and the Edward R. Roybal Centers for Research on Applied Gerontology.

GERIATRIC CARE

The size of the population over 65 years of age has grown from 4.1% in 1900 to 12.6% in 2000. By 2030 it is estimated that 20% of the population will be 65 years and older. This increase in the number of older persons has been accompanied by a marked increase in life span such that the average life expectancy at the age of 65 is 19.4 years for females and 16.4 years for males. In addition, the presence of chronic disabilities in the population over 65 years of age has declined.

Geriatric care systems in the United States began in 1861 with the development of the military pension system for Civil War veterans. In 1930, this system became the Veteran's Administration, which has remained a leader in the development of modern geriatric care. The first nursing home in the United States was the Lafon Asylum of the Holy Family, which was opened in New Orleans in 1942. Government pensions for older persons were started by the Social Security Board, which became the Social Security Administration in 1946. In 1965 the development of Medicare and Medicaid guaranteed government-funded health care to older adults.

A number of specialized programs to improve care of older persons in the United States have been developed. These include Acute Care for the Elderly (ACE) Units (Landefeld, Palmer, Kresevic, Fortinksy, & Kowal, 1995), Delirium Intensive Care Units (Flaherty et al., 2003), Sub-acute care centers or units (Makowski, Maggard, & Morley, 2000), Geriatric Evaluation and Management Units (GEMU; Rubenstein et al., 1984), Geriatric-Friendly Nurses in the Emergency Department (Miller, Lewis, Nork, & Morley, 1996), and Programs of All Inclusive Care for the Elderly (PACE; Eng, Pedulla, Eleazer, McCann, & Fox, 1997). In addition, the United States has been a leader in establishing screening tools for geriatric assessment (see Table 3.1). Two attempts to standardize geriatric care in hospitals and outpatients are the ACOVE guidelines (Morley, 2008; Wenger, Roth, & Shekelle, 2007) and the Glidepaths (Flaherty, Morley, Murphy, & Wasserman, 2002).

Four percent of persons over 65 years of age live in nursing homes. In the United States there are approximately 18,000 nursing homes, with an average of 100 beds in each nursing home. Most of the nursing home care (68%) is paid for by the government. The 1987 Omnibus Budget Reconciliation Act created a variety of regulations for nursing homes aimed at improving quality of care. This led to the establishment of the Minimum Data Set (MDS) for Nursing Home Residents. Nursing homes have been leaders in the establishment of continuous quality improvement programs (Morley, Flaherty, & Thomas, 2003; Schnelle, 2007). The development of the Eden Alternative led to de-emphasis of the medical aspects of nursing homes and increased emphasis of their home-like aspects. Nursing homes using this approach encourage pets and provide gardens for the residents to work in. Empowerment of nurses and residents to be innovative in developing their care plans is a key component of this model. Another nursing home innovation was the so-called Beers list of inappropriate drugs for older persons in nursing homes (Beers et al., 1992; Fick et al., 2003). Assisted-living facilities are largely unregulated residential care facilities where the residents tend to need a less medically intensive level of care. They tend to be expensive, and quality of care is variable (Schumacher, 2006).

Home care by physicians in the United States was first formalized by the Homeopathic Medical Center in 1875. This program has metamorphosed

TABLE 3.1

Screening Tools for Geriatric Assessment Developed in the United States

Date	Scale	Reference
1955	Barthel Index	Goldberg, Bernad, & Granger (1980); Mahoney & Barthel (1965)
1963	Activities of Daily Living	Katz, Ford, Moskowitz, Jackson, & Jaffe (1963); Katz, Downs, Cash, & Grotz (1970)
1969	Instrumental Activities of Daily Living	Lawton & Brody (1969)
1975	Mini-Mental Status	Folstein, Folstein, & McHugh (1975)
1983	Geriatric Depression Scale	Yesavage et al. (1982–1983)
1986	Performance-Oriented Assessment of Mobility	Tinetti (1986)
2000	Androgen Deficiency in Aging Males (ADAM)	Morley et al. (2000)
2003	Saint Louis University Mental Status (SLUMS) test	Tariq, Tumosa, Chibnall, Perry, & Morley (2006)
2005	Simplified Nutrition Assessment Questionnaire	Wilson et al. (2005)
2007	Dehydration Screen	Thomas et al. (2008)

over the years from originally providing obstetrical and pediatric visits into a model center for geriatric home care. This change took place under the leadership of Knight Steel at what is now called the Boston University Medical Center (Steel, 1987). Modern home care is provided predominantly by nurses and physical therapists (e.g., fall-prevention programs) with less than 1% of physician health care occurring in the home (Leff & Burton, 2001). Home visits have been demonstrated to be useful for preventive care, which results in a delay in functional decline (Fabacher, Josephson, & Pietruszka, 1994; Stuck et al., 1995). Telemedicine is beginning to emerge, under leadership of the Veterans Administration, as a new approach to delivering home care.

The need for better training in geriatrics is evident in the statistics. Older persons account for half of all hospitalization days, one-third of total health care expenditures, and one-quarter of all outpatient encounters. The number of outpatient visits increases with age from 5.2 at 65–75 years to 6.8 at over

75 years of age. Outpatients visits are provided by internists and family practitioners, but nearly half of these visits are by specialists (e.g., ophthalmologists, cardiologists, and urologists). The need for increasing the awareness of geriatric principles in these specialists is obvious. It is worth noting that in a survey of 12,474 physicians in the late 1990s, it was found that geriatric internal medicine physicians were found to consider their practice very satisfactory more often than any other specialty (Leigh, Kravitz, Schembri, Samuels, & Mobley, 2002).

MEDICAL STUDENT EDUCATION

Despite the so-called age wave occurring in the United States population, the integration of geriatrics into medical schools has been relatively slow. In 1998, while most medical schools reported some geriatric medicine in their curriculum, the American Association of Medical Colleges reported that required geriatric courses remained rare.

A snapshot of the penetration of geriatric medical education can be obtained from the Medical School Graduation Questionnaire of the Association of American Medical Colleges (AAMC; see Figure 3.1). This questionnaire indicates that most (75% or more) graduating students agree or strongly agree that geriatrics is covered adequately in their medicine or family medicine rotations. However, the breadth of practice sites and duration of exposure were rated somewhat lower ("no opinion" or "agree") in exposure to long-term care or interdisciplinary setting and exposure over the 4 years of medical school) (AAMC, 2006).

While there is a clear improvement in geriatrics education, the penetration of geriatrics remains inadequate. In particular, there is a shortage of required clinical exposure to geriatrics. Much of the penetration of geriatrics is the occasional lecture inserted in occasional courses rather than a specific geriatrics block experience. One study suggested a geriatric block experience had greater impact than a longitudinal experience (Steinweg, Cummings, & Kelly, 2001). The majority of published material on longitudinal versus block rotations exists in graduate medical education (GME) primarily in the areas of family and internal medicine. Most articles describe block rotation experiences of 4 weeks' duration. The breadth of longitudinal geriatrics experiences described in the literature is vast and not standardized to one particular methodology (e.g., mentor programs or didactics for preclinical students, patient encounters in GME, or a geriatric scholar program).

The Association of Directors of Geriatric Academic Programs' (ADGAP) Geriatric Workforce Study data indicates that there is a significant barrier to implementing geriatric medicine education programs across the country and

1. I learned about the health care needs of healthy older adults during my medical training.

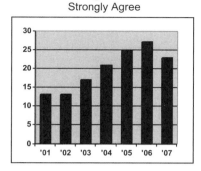

Strongly Agree

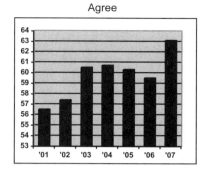

Agree

2. I am well prepared to care for older adult patients in acute care settings.

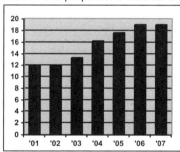

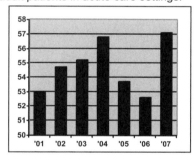

3. I am well prepared to care for older adult patients in ambulatory settings.

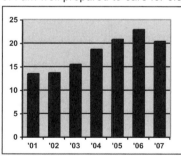

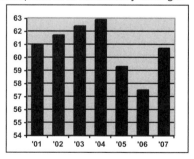

FIGURE 3.1 Survey data from the Medical School Graduation Questionnaire done by the Association of American Medical Colleges.
Note. Number of respondents for each year were as follows: 2001: *n* = 14,156; 2002: *n* = 14,169; 2003: *n* = 13,646; 2004: *n* = 10,706; 2005: *n* = 9,459; 2006: *n* = 11,411; 2007: *n* = 12,511. From "Survey Data from the Medical School Graduation Questionnaire," by the Association of American Medical Colleges, 2008, http://www.aamc.org/data/gq/allschoolsreports/start.htm (Accessed January 20, 2008).

4. I am well prepared to care for older adults patients in long-term health care settings.

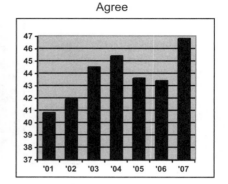

5. I was exposed to expert geriatric care by the attending faculty of my medical program.

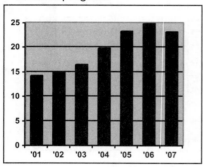
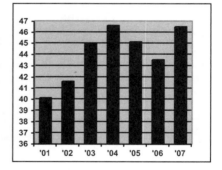

6. Geriatric/gerontology education was part of all 4 years of my medical education.

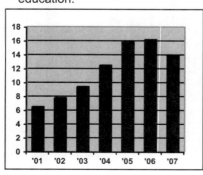
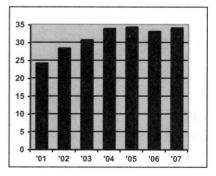

FIGURE 3.1 *(continued)*

that most programs have limited access to the medical student curriculum (ADGAP, 2002). Moreover, schools are recognizing the need for geriatric medicine, and the time dedicated to geriatrics in the curriculum has increased, but student perception is that their exposure to geriatrics is limited despite this fact (Eleazer, Doshi, Wieland, Boland, & Hirth, 2005).

Medical schools remain far more interested in teaching students about the latest advances in subspecialty medicine and basic science than they do in teaching the core components necessary for a student to become a competent primary care physician. In addition, many faculty tend to believe that because they see many older patients they automatically know how to care for them, even while they remain untrained in most principles of geriatric care.

A major innovation in teaching geriatrics has been the introduction of educational games (Tumosa & Morley, 2006). The interactive Aging Game has been particularly successful (Pacala, Boult, & Hepburn, 2006; Varkey, Chutka, & Lesnick, 2006). Other games include Geropady, the Geriatric Challenge Bowl and the 3 D's of cognitive impairment card sorting game (Paniagua, Pua, van Zuilen, Mintzer, & Silver, 2006). Some of these games are particularly useful in improving attitudes to older persons (Tumosa & Morley, 2006). Exposing medical students to healthy, highly successful aging persons has also proved to be an important tool in enhancing positive feelings about geriatrics (Flaherty & Wilson, 2004).

RESIDENT EDUCATION

Geriatric training in internal medicine residency programs remains limited (Bragg, Warshaw, Arenson, Ho, & Brewer, 2006). Nine percent of programs require less than 2 weeks of clinical instruction, 21% require between 2 and 4 weeks, 62% require between 4 and 6 weeks, and 9% require 6 or more weeks. Training was most often offered in a block format. Major teaching sites were nursing homes, outpatient clinics, and geriatric preceptorships in nongeriatric ambulatory settings. The average number of full-time geriatric teachers was 3.5, which was 1.3 times greater than the number reported 3 years before.

In contrast, family medicine programs in 2004 had on average only 0.9 full-time equivalents in geriatrics (Bragg, Warshaw, Arenson, Ho, & Brewer, 2006). Ninety-six percent of programs reported that they had a required geriatrics curriculum.

SUBSPECIALTY RESIDENTS IN GERIATRIC MEDICINE AND GERIATRIC PSYCHIATRY

There are 139 programs offering subspecialty training in geriatrics in either internal medicine or family medicine (see Table 3.2; ADGAP, 2007).

TABLE 3.2
Geriatric Medicine Subspecialty Residency Programs

Year	Programs	Fellows	IMGs (%)
1991–1992	92	198	32.3
1996–1997	103	242	59.9
2002–2003	127	368	51.6
2006–2007	139	287	64.1

Note. IMGs = International medical graduates

In 1998 the geriatric fellowship was reduced from 2 years to 1 year despite the strong opposition of those who felt that this would erode the academic standing of geriatrics. This experiment is now widely accepted as a failure, but as yet the geriatrics leadership has been unable to reverse the situation (Morley, 1993).

Despite the existence of 139 fellowship programs, 46% of all first-year positions are not filled. In the last 5 years there has been a 22% decrease in the number of fellows in training. There were only 34 fellows enrolled in a second year of training in 2006–2007, representing a 55% decrease since 2002–2003. International medical graduates (IMGs) have been increasing as a percentage of the total fellows, and in 2006–2007 comprised 64.1% of the total.

The influx of IMGs into geriatric fellowships is disturbing because results from postcompletion surveys are suggesting that many IMGs are using this year either to find a job that will give them a visa waiver or alternatively to stay employed while they wait for positions in different subspecialty fellowships.

The condition of geriatric psychiatry mirrors that of geriatric medicine fellowships. There were 58 geriatric psychiatry fellowship programs with 72 fellows in 2006–2007. IMGs represented 61.1% of all trainees. Fifty-two percent of all available positions remained unfilled.

It has been estimated that the United States needs 36,000 geriatricians by 2030. In 2007 there were 7,128 certified geriatricians and 1,596 certified geriatric psychiatrists (ADGAP, 2008). Based on current graduation rates, it is estimated that in 2030 there would be 7,750 geriatricians and 1,659 geriatric psychiatrists. Given the rapid aging of the population, this will mean that there will be 1 geriatrician for every 4,254 older Americans compared to 1 for every 2,546 older patients at the present time. In addition, there has been a decline in the pass rate of the geriatric boards from 86% in 2002 to 78% in 2005. This was the lowest pass mark in the subspecialty boards.

Unfortunately, these statistics represent an extraordinarily bleak picture for geriatrics in the future. There is a clear mandate for new and innovative approaches to enhancing the numbers of quality geriatric faculty in the future.

ACADEMIC FACULTY

The mean number of physician faculty in geriatric medicine is 10.1 in allopathic schools and 5.6 in osteopathic schools; the mean number of research faculty in allopathic schools is 3.7 and 1.1 in osteopathic schools (ADGAP, 2006a, 2006b). In allopathic schools 10% of time is allocated to medical student education, 10% to residency education, and 10% to fellowship training. In osteopathic schools the percentages are 20%, 5%, and 2.5%, respectively. Clinical practice time in geriatrics is 39% in allopathic schools and 45% in osteopathic schools. Research time is 15% and 5%, respectively. There has been increased program support from clinical practice reaching 32% in 2005 with an additional 17% coming from the Veterans Administration. Overall budgets were variable, with 65% reporting budgets less than $2 million and 35% reporting greater than $2 million. Directors of academic programs in geriatrics reported their three major obstacles to increasing their budget for geriatric teaching, research, and clinical care were poor clinical reimbursement for patient care, lack of research fellows in geriatrics, and lack of senior faculty.

There are limited programs for development of geriatric faculty. The most successful have been the Geriatric Academic Career Award (GACA) program sponsored by the Department of Health and Human Services, Health Resource and Services Administration (HRSA). There is also the 2-year Geriatric Training for Faculty in Medicine, Dentistry and Behavioral/Mental Health Fellowship, which is also funded by HRSA. The Veterans Administration also has a 3-year research faculty development program that is run through the Geriatric Research, Education and Clinical Centers. The Donald W. Reynolds Foundation has developed a number of short courses for faculty, and Saint Louis University School of Medicine has implemented a successful program, the Saint Louis University Geriatrics Academy (SLUGA), based on the European Academy of Geriatric Medicine program (Gammack et al., 2004; Swine, Michel, Duursma, Grimley Evans, & Staehelin, 2004).

The limited research success of geriatrics programs in the United States can be gauged by examining the geriatricians with the highest citations to their articles (see Table 3.3; Morley, 2007).

TABLE 3.3

2007 Editorial Board Members of the Journals of Gerontology: Medical Sciences, Journal of the American Geriatrics Society, Age and Aging, American Journal of Geriatric Psychiatry, *and* Alzheimer Disease and Associated Disorders *as well as the 2007 expanded editorial board of the* Journal of the American Medical Directors Association, *who were cited more than 2,000 times from 1995 to 2006.*

Name	Discipline	No. of Papers	Citations	Average[a]	h-Index[b]
Barrett-Connor, E.	Family Practice	408	9,056	22.2	42
Cummings, J. L.	Neurology	379	8,976	23.68	49
Morris, J. C.	Neurology	262	8,617	32.9	44
Petersen, R. C.	Neurology	196	7,449	38.01	39
Guralnik, J. M.	Geriatrics	361	7,444	21.17	45
DeKosky, S. T.	Neurology	330	7,025	21.29	44
McKeith, I.	Neurology	219	6,119	28.33	37
Morley, J. E.	Geriatrics	343	6,012	17.53	40
Longo, D. L.	Oncology	222	5,920	27.53	42
Reynolds III, C. F.	Psychiatry	319	5,628	17.64	38
Ferrucci, L.	Geriatrics	329	5,160	15.00	37
Jeste, D. V.	Psychiatry	317	4,790	15.11	35
Martin, G. M.	Geriatrics	163	4,753	29.16	32
Harris, T. B.	Epidemiology	236	4,585	19.43	34
King, A. C.	Epidemiology	106	4,396	41.47	27
Fried, L.	Geriatrics	271	4,384	16.18	35
Wallace, R. B.	Geriatrics	116	4,224	36.41	31
Tangalos, E. G.	Geriatrics	88	3,966	45.07	23
Raskind, M.	Psychiatry	125	3,874	30.99	28
Newman, A. B.	Geriatrics	170	3,849	13.95	31
Pahor, M.	Geriatrics	220	3,848	17.49	32
Scheltens, P.	Neurology	275	3,760	13.76	39
Rich, M. W.	Cardiology	129	3,757	29.12	24
Kukull, W.	Neurology	95	3,387	35.65	24
Tinetti, M. E.	Geriatrics	100	3,386	33.86	31
Paolisso, G.	Geriatrics	141	3,322	23.56	31
Nordberg, A.	Neurology	182	3,304	18.15	31
Landefeld, C. S.	Geriatrics	96	3,145	32.76	27

(continued)

TABLE 3.3 (Continued)

Metter, E. J.	Neurology	128	3,135	24.49	30
Blazer, D. G.	Psychiatry	136	3,130	23.01	29
Wilcock, G.	Neurology	118	3,105	26.31	22
Erkinjuntti, T.	Neurology	138	3,012	21.83	30
Arndt, S.	Psychiatry	192	2,948	22.33	31
Korczyn, A. D.	Neurology	340	2,918	8.58	27
Rockwood, K.	Geriatrics	210	2,878	13.70	29
Barzilai, N.	Endocrinology	97	2,839	29.27	28
Yaffe, K.	Psychiatry	168	2,832	16.86	27
Gandy, S. E.	Neurology	50	2,800	56.00	22
Lipsitz, L. A.	Geriatrics	128	2,765	21.04	28
Fox, N.	Neurology	160	2,765	17.28	31
Penninx, B. W. J. H.	Geriatrics	129	2,740	21.24	31
Simonsick, E. M.	Geriatrics	106	2,669	25.10	20
Cohen, H. J.	Geriatrics	170	2,609	14.82	26
Seeman, T. A.	Geriatrics	114	2,607	22.87	31
Mulsant, B. H.	Psychiatry	193	2,600	13.47	28
Doody, R. S.	Neurology	67	2,598	38.78	17
Baumgartner, R. N.	Gerontology	114	2,562	22.47	30
Herrup, K.	Gerontology	54	2,521	46.69	23
Launer, L.	Epidemiology	93	2,395	25.65	26
Gilman, S.	Epidemiology	93	2,323	24.96	22
Lyketsos, C. G.	Psychiatry	174	2,315	13.38	27
Roher, A. E.	Biologist	62	2,277	36.73	27
Inouye, S. K.	Geriatrics	94	2,220	23.62	24
Steffens, D.	Psychiatry	132	2,219	16.81	23
Balducci, L.	Oncology	128	2,158	16.86	22
Visser, M.	Neurology	120	2,132	19.99	29
Resnick, B.	Geriatrics	107	2093	19.54	23
Corti, M. C.	Rheumatology	42	2,044	48.67	19
Ganguli, M.	Psychiatry	93	2,040	21.94	26
Evans, W. J.	Gerontology	135	2,036	15.08	27

[a]Average number of citations per paper. [b]The h-index is the number of papers a scientist has published that have been cited at least the same number of times.

FUTURE HISTORY

The predictions for the future of geriatrics must be based on the past, though quixotic occurrences can produce extraordinarily different outcomes from those predicted. With this caveat, we would like to suggest the following possible future history of geriatrics:

1. The demographic imperative and, in particular, the arrival of the baby boomer generation, will continue to drive the need for geriatricians. However, history has proven that need alone is inadequate to produce the requisite number of geriatricians.
2. Geriatricians need to reclaim a place at the academic table. This requires returning to a 2-year fellowship and increasing the quantity and quality of research carried out by geriatricians. Failing this, geriatrics will develop into a separate area akin to pediatrics. Geriatric hospitals and rehabilitation centers will become the major areas of practice for future geriatricians.
3. Geriatrics needs to have a major role in medical school curricula. This is in and of itself a demographic imperative. It needs to include at least a month-long clinical geriatric and rehabilitation block, with well-aligned continuity clinical experiences among complementary rotations.
4. Reimbursement for geriatricians needs to increase so that it is preferable to go into geriatrics rather than into other subspecialties. To do this, geriatrics needs to develop and control a series of special tests such as a frailty battery, mobility tests, nutritional testing, and tests of cognitive function.
5. Geriatricians need to be consistently in the public eye—marketing is the American way.
6. Geriatrics needs to develop a true evidence base—not just accepting evidence that has been gathered in younger persons. The development of these intervention studies needs to be controlled by geriatricians.
7. Geriatrics education needs to be truly evidence-based, and geriatricians need to claim their place based on evidence, rather than by argument.
8. A way to convert successful mid-career faculty to geriatricians needs to be developed.
9. Geriatricians need to embrace new technologies and procedures for nursing home and home-based care while responding to patient-driven demands to develop alternative health care models that include palliative care, rehabilitation, and dementia care.

Overall, geriatrics is an extraordinarily exciting and happy subspecialty. It is up to academic geriatricians to transmit this feeling to students, residents, and other health professions learners.

Those who cannot remember the past are condemned to repeat it.
—George Santayana (1905)

REFERENCES

Association of American Medical College. (2006). *Medical student graduation questionnaire*. Retrieved January 20, 2008, from http://www.aamc.org/data/gq/allschools reports/start.htm

Association of Directors of Geriatric Academic Programs. (2002). *Geriatric medicine training and practice in the United States at the beginning of the 21st century*. Retrieved January 4, 2008, from http://www.adgapstudy.uc.edu/Files/ADGAP %20Full%20Report.pdf

Association of Directors of Geriatric Academic Programs. (2006a). Fellows in geriatric medicine and geriatric psychiatry programs. The status of geriatrics workforce study. *Training and Practice Update, 4*(2). Retrieved September 12, 2007, from http://www.adgapstudy.uc.edu/Files/ADGAP%20Training%20and%20Practice %update%204_2.pdf

Association of Directors of Geriatric Academic Programs. (2006b). Fellows in geriatric medicine and geriatric psychiatry programs. The status of geriatrics workforce study. *Training and Practice Update, 4*(1). Retrieved September 12, 2007, from http://www.adgapstudy.uc.edu/Files/ADGAP%20Training%20and%20Practice %update%204_1.pdf

Association of Directors of Geriatric Academic Programs. (2007). Fellows in geriatric medicine and geriatric psychiatry programs. The status of geriatrics workforce study. *Training and Practice Update, 5*(2). Retrieved September 12, 2007, from ttp://www.adgapstudy.uc.edu/Files/ADGAP%20Training%20and%20Practice %update%205_2.pdf

Beers, M. H., Ouslander, J. G., Fingold, S. F., Morgenstern, H., Reuben, D. B., Rogers, W., et al. (1992). Inappropriate medication prescribing in skilled-nursing facilities. *Annals of Internal Medicine, 117*, 684–689.

Bragg, E. J., Warshaw, G. A., Arenson, C., Ho, M. L., & Brewer, D. E. (2006). A national survey of family medicine residency education in geriatric medicine: Comparing findings in 2004 to 2001. *Family Medicine, 38*, 258–264.

Eleazer, G. P., Doshi, R., Wieland, D., Boland, R., & Hirth, V. A. (2005). Geriatric content in medical school curricula: Results of a national survey. *Journal of the American Geriatrics Society, 53*(1), 136–140.

Eng, C., Pedulla, J., Eleazer, G. P., et al. (1997). Program of All-inclusive Care for the Elderly (PACE): An innovative model of integrated geriatric care and financing. *Journal of the American Geriatrics Society, 45,* 223–232.

Fabacher, D., Josephson, K., & Pietruszka, F. (1994). An in-home preventive assessment program for independent older adults: A randomized controlled trial. *Journal of the American Geriatrics Society, 42,* 630–638.

Fick, D. M., Cooper, J. W., Wade, W. E., Waller, J. L., Maclean, J. R., & Beers, M. H. (2003). Updating the Beers criteria for potentially inappropriate medication use in older adults: Results of a US consensus panel of experts. *Archives of Internal Medicine, 163,* 2716–2724.

Flaherty, J. H., Morley, J. E., Murphy, D. J., & Wasserman, M. R. (2002). The development of outpatient clinical Glidepaths. *Journal of the American Geriatrics Society, 50,* 1886–1901.

Flaherty, J. H., Tariq, S. H., Raghavan, S., Bakshi, S., Moinudden, A., & Morley, J. E. (2003). A model for managing delirious older inpatients. *Journal of the American Geriatrics Society, 51,* 1031–1035.

Flaherty, J. H., & Wilson, M. M. (2004). Saint Louis University School of Medicine. *Academic Medicine, 79,* S168–S172.

Folstein, M. F., Folstein, S. E., & McHugh, P. R. (1975). Mini-Mental State. A practical method for grading the cognitive state of patients for the clinician. *Journal of Psychological Research, 12,* 189–198.

Gammack, J. K., Rudolph, J. L., Adedokun, A., Hirth, V., Kevorkian, R., & Misra, S. (2004). Perceptions of geriatric medicine junior faculty on success in academic medicine: The Saint Louis University Geriatric Academy (SLUGA) faculty development program. *Journal of Gerontology Series A: Biological Sciences and Medical Sciences, 59,* 1029–1035.

Goldberg, R. T., Bernad, M., & Granger, C. V. (1980). Vocational status: Prediction by the Barthel index and PULSES profile. *Archives of Physical Medicine and Rehabilitation, 61,* 580–583.

Katz, S., Downs, T. D., Cash, H. R., & Grotz, R. C. (1970). Progress in development of the index of ADL. *Gerontologist, 10,* 20–30.

Katz, S., Ford, A. B., Moskowitz, R. W., Jackson, B. A., & Jaffe, M. W. (1963). Studies of illness in the aged: The Index of ADL: A standardized measure of biological and psychosocial function. *Journal of the American Medical Association, 185,* 914–919.

Landefeld, C. S., Palmer, R. M., Kresevic, D. M., Fortinsky, R. H., & Kowal, J. (1995). A randomized trial of care in a hospital medical unit especially designed to improve the functional outcomes of acutely ill older patients. *New England Journal of Medicine, 332,* 1338–1344.

Lawton, M. P., & Brody, E. M. (1969). Assessment of older people self maintaining and instrumental activities of daily living. *Gerontologist, 9,* 179–186.

Leff, B., & Burton, J. R. (2001). The future history of home care and physician house calls in the United States. *Journal of Gerontology Series A: Biological Sciences and Medical Sciences, 56,* M603–M608.

Leigh, J. P., Kravitz, R. L., Schembri, M., Samuels, S. J., & Mobley, S. (2002). Physician career satisfaction across specialties. *Archives of Internal Medicine, 162,* 1577–1584.

Mahoney, F. I., & Barthel, D. W. (1965). Functional evaluation: The Barthel Index. *Maryland State Medical Journal, 14,* 61–65.

Makowski, T. R., Maggard, W., & Morley, J. E. (2000). The Life Care Center of St. Louis experience with subacute care. *Clinical Geriatric Medicine, 16,* 701–724.

Miller, D. K., Lewis, L. M., Nork, M. J., & Morley, J. E. (1996). Controlled trial of a geriatric case-finding and liaison service in an emergency department. *Journal of the American Geriatrics Society, 44,* 513–520.

Morley, J. E. (1993). Geriatric medicine: A true subspecialty. *Journal of the American Geriatrics Society, 41,* 1150–1154.

Morley, J. E. (2004). A brief history of geriatrics. *Journal of Gerontology Series A: Biological Sciences and Medical Sciences, 59,* 1132–1152.

Morley, J. E. (2007). The future history of long term care. *Journal of the American Medical Director's Association, 8,* 553–556.

Morley, J. E. (2008). Caring for the vulnerable elderly: Are available quality indicators appropriate? *Journal of the American Medical Director's Association, 9,* 1–3.

Morley, J. E., Charlton, E., Patrick, P., Kaiser, F. E., Cadeau, P., McCready, D., et al. (2000). Validation of a screening questionnaire for androgen deficiency in aging males. *Metabolism: Clinical and Experimental, 49,* 1239–1242.

Morley, J. E., Flaherty, J. H., & Thomas, D. R. (2003). Geriatricians, continuous quality improvement, and improved care for older persons. *Journal of Gerontology Series A: Biological Sciences and Medical Sciences, 58,* M809–M812.

Morley, J. E., & Gammack, J. K. (2006). Geriatrics in the United States. In M. S. J. Pathy, A. J. Sinclair, & J. E. Morley (Eds.), *Principles and practice of geriatric medicine* (4th ed.). West Sussex, England: John Wiley & Sons.

Nascher, I. L. (1909). Longevity and rejuvenescence. *New York Medical Journal, 89,* 795-800.

Pacala, J. T., Boult, C., & Hepburn, K. (2006). Ten years' experience conducting the Aging Game workshop: Was it worth it? *Journal of the American Geriatrics Society, 54,* 144–149.

Paniagua, M., Pua, R. J., van Zuilen, M., Mintzer, M. J., & Silver, I. (2006). *"The three D's" of cognitive impairment: An interactive card-sorting exercise.* Retrieved October 8, 2008, from http://services.aamc.org/jsp/mededportal/searchUserInfo.do

Rubenstein, L. Z., Josephson, K. R., Wieland, G. D., English, P. A., Sayre, J. A., & Kane, R. L. (1984). Effectiveness of a geriatric evaluation unit. A randomized clinical trial. *New England Journal of Medicine, 311,* 1664–1670.

Santayana, G. (1905). *The life of reason. Vol 1.* New York: Charles Scribner's Son's.

Schnelle, J. F. (2007). Continuous quality improvement in nursing homes: Public relations or a reality? *Journal of the American Medical Director's Association,* 8(3 Suppl.), S2–S5.

Schumacher, J. G. (2006). Examining the physician's role with assisted living residents. *Journal of the American Medical Director's Association, 7,* 377–382.

Steel, K. (1987). Physician-directed long-term home health care for the elderly—a century-long experience. *Journal of the American Geriatrics Society, 35,* 264–268.

Steinweg, K. K., Cummings, D. M., & Kelly, S. K. (2001). Are some subjects better taught in block rotation? A geriatric experience. *Family Medicine, 33,* 756–761.

Stuck, A. E., Aronow, H. U., Steiner, A., Alessi, C. A., Bula, C. J., Gold, M. N., et al. (1995). A trial of annual in-home comprehensive geriatric assessments for elderly people living in the community. *New England Journal of Medicine, 333,* 1184–1189.

Swine, C., Michel, J. P., Duursma, S., Grimley Evans, J., & Staehelin, H. B. (2004). Evaluation of the European Academy for Medicine of Ageing "Teaching the Teachers" program (EAMA course II 1997–1998). *Journal of Nutrition, Health and Aging, 8,* 181–186.

Tariq, S. H., Tumosa, N., Chibnall, J. T., Perry III, M. H., & Morley, J. E. (2006). Comparison of the SLU Mental Status Examination and the Mini-Mental Status Examination for detecting dementia and mild neurocognitive disorder—a pilot study. *American Journal of Geriatric Psychiatry, 14,* 900–910.

Thomas, D. R., Cote, T. R., Lawhorne, L., Levenson, S. A., Rubenstein, L. Z., Smith, D. A., et al. (2008). Understanding clinical dehydration and its treatment. *Journal of the American Medical Director's Association, 9,* 292–301.

Tinetti, M. E. (1986). Performance-oriented assessment of mobility problems in elderly patients. *Journal of the American Geriatrics Society, 34,* 119–126.

Toffler, A. (1980). *The third wave.* New York: Bantam Books.

Tumosa, N., & Morley, J. E. (2006). The use of games to improve patient outcomes. *Gerontological Geriatric Education, 26,* 37–45.

Varkey, P., Chutka, D. S., Lesnick, T. G. (2006). The Aging Game: Improving medical students' attitudes toward caring for the elderly. *Journal of the American Medical Director's Association, 7,* 224–229.

Warshaw, G. A., Bragg, E. J., Thomas, D. C., Ho, M. L., & Brewer, D. E. (2006). Are internal medicine residency programs adequately preparing physicians to care for the baby boomers? A national survey from the Association of Directors of Geriatric Academic Programs Status of Geriatrics Workforce Study. *Journal of the American Geriatrics Society, 54,* 1603–1609.

Wenger, N. S., Roth, C. P., & Shekelle, P. (2007). ACOVE investigators. Introduction to the assessing care of vulnerable elders-3 quality indicator measurement set. *Journal of the American Geriatrics Society, 55*(Suppl. 2), S247–S252.

Wilson, M. M. Thomas, D. R., Rubenstein, L. Z., Chibnell, J. T., Anderson, S., & Baxi, A. (2005). Appetite assessment: Simple appetite questionnaire predicts weight loss in community-dwelling adults and NH residents. *American Journal of Clinical Nutrition, 82,* 1074–1081.

Yesavage, J. A., Brink, T. L., Rose, T. L., Lum, O., Huang, V., Adley, M., et al. (1982–1983). Development and validation of a Geriatric Depression Scale: A preliminary report. *Journal of Psychological Research, 17,* 37–49.

CHAPTER 4

Global Aging and Gerontology Education

The International Mandate

Suzanne R. Kunkel

Global aging is a revolutionary phenomenon that has implications for all aspects of life. Societal responses to the challenges and opportunities of an aging population require decision-makers, researchers, planners and designers, service providers, political leaders, and citizens who are educated about aging. Indeed, Aristotle advised that, "Education is the best provision for old age" (Laertius, 2008). This statement is advice for those who would have a fulfilling old age: a rich intellectual life is a valuable provision to carry on the journey to old age. But, we can generalize Aristotle's advice to suggest that education about aging is essential for thoughtful and effective *societal* responses to aging. To meet the need for a population educated about aging and to be better able to design policies and programs to address an aging society, academic programs in gerontology are being developed around the world.

Paralleling the unprecedented number of nations seeing growth in gerontology education is an increased value placed on global and comparative perspectives *within* education about aging. Gerontology programs are increasingly adding global content to their courses, and more programs than even are adding international study programs to their curricula. The prominence of international aging in the field of gerontology is reflected in

DOI: 10.1891/0198-8794.28.45

the fact that two of the premier national U.S. organizations and one international organization have focused efforts on these issues. In 2007, the theme of the Gerontological Society of America's annual meeting was "The Era of Global Aging: Challenges and Opportunities"; in 2004, the Association for Gerontology in Higher Education (AGHE) organized its annual leadership conference around the theme of "Global Aging." For more than 5 years, AGHE has had an International Task Force to facilitate collaborations and partnerships to meet the global need for education and training about aging. The International Association of Gerontology and Geriatrics (IAGG) organizes a world congress every 4 years to advance research and education on aging, and to foster cross-national collaboration in these areas. The IAGG Web site provides a listing of gerontology programs around the world. The Association for Anthropology and Gerontology (AAGE) has a strong commitment to "the exploration and understanding of aging within and across diverse cultures" (Shenk & Groger, 2005, p. 6), and offers a range of resources for individuals interested in teaching gerontology from a comparative global perspective. A recent conference in Okinawa, Japan, focused heavily on the development of international gerontology curriculum, and an upcoming 2009 conference in India will include a strong gerontology education focus.

The involvement of national and international organizations and the emerging body of publications and resources to foster collaborations and facilitate teaching about international and cross-national aging reinforce the fact that gerontology is becoming a globalized field of study. Indeed, three undeniable and interrelated trends—rapid global aging and its associated opportunities and challenges, the rise in gerontology programs around the world, and the increasing internationalization of gerontology programs—speak to an international mandate for gerontology in higher education. These three phenomena are the focus of this chapter.

A brief discussion about the demographic implications of global aging sets the stage for an overview of the development of gerontology programs in different regions of the world; such programs, as responses to societal and individual aging, can support the development of culturally appropriate policies and service systems to meet needs of growing older populations and can help to prepare a work force to meet needs of aging society. The very diversity and complexity of aging experiences around the world help to make a case for the third aspect of the international mandate for gerontology and higher education: the value of incorporating cross-national content and international educational experiences within gerontology programs.

GLOBAL AGING: THE NEED FOR EDUCATION ABOUT AGING

We live in an aging world. In the next decade or so, the number of people 65 years and older will exceed the number of children for the first time in human history, and it is projected that the world will have 1 billion older people by the year 2030 (National Institute on Aging [NIA], 2007). With very rare exceptions, every nation in the world is aging, and the most rapid rate of growth in aging populations is occurring in the developing nations. These regions of the world will see a 140% increase in their older population by the year 2030 (NIA, 2007).

The number and proportion of older people, and life expectancy, are useful measures of population aging and can be indicative of the issues that are likely to be at the forefront of public policy and resource allocation. Information from a United Nations Population Division 2002 publication (United Nations [UN], 2002) helps to illustrate this point. Italy, with 18% of its population aged 65 and over and a life expectancy of almost 79 is likely dealing with very different economic, infrastructure, and health care issues than is Kenya with 2.8% of its people over the age of 65 and a life expectancy of 49. It is safe to assume that maternal and child health issues are of much more immediate concern in Kenya, while Italy is immersed in the workforce, health care, and caregiving challenges of an aging population. As immediate as aging issues in Italy are, they will increase in salience; by 2050, Italy is expected to have an older population that represents nearly 36% of its total population.

These measures of population age structure are very instructive, conveying some sense of the current challenges facing each society. But the rate at which a society is growing older is perhaps a better indication of the social changes and challenges about which gerontology education can be essential. For example, between the years of 1950 and 2003, life expectancy for women in China increased from 42 to 73. Over that same time frame, U.S. women experienced an increase in life expectancy from 72 to 80 (Kinsella & Phillips, 2005). The 30-year gain in longevity for Chinese women, over a relatively short time period, connotes enormous, consequential, and very rapid demographic and social change. The speed of population aging—the rapidity with which a nation transforms into an aging society—has obvious corollaries in the nature and urgency of the challenges each society will face. In general, the developing world is aging much more rapidly than the developed regions. For example, it took France 115 years for the proportion of its population that is 65 and older to rise from 7% to 14%. The United States underwent this transformation in 69 years. Sri Lanka, Thailand, Brazil, and Singapore will all experience this change in less than 25 years. Japan, by all measures one of the oldest nations in the world, went through this transformation in 26 years (Kinsella & Phillips, 2005). It is easy to imagine the vast array of changes that precipitate, and result from, such rapid population aging and the role played by economic and cultural forces in both causes and consequences of this dramatic demographic shift. At a minimum, countries that age at such precipitous rates have less time to adapt to, much less anticipate, the consequences of population aging. The mandates for education about aging are certainly affected by the nature and speed of population aging, because different challenges will be of different urgency. As we will see, rapidly aging nations often focus first on developing education and training programs to meet the very pressing needs for health care workers.

Recent scholarship on global aging highlights the range of challenges that accompany the successes of increased longevity. These challenges include: an increase in the oldest old; the dominance of chronic diseases (rather than communicable diseases) as the major cause of death; health care systems that are ill-prepared and poorly designed for chronic care; persistent ageism; shifting patterns of work and retirement; vulnerable social insurance programs; and far-reaching economic challenges (Butler, 2008; Kinsella & Phillips, 2002; NIA, 2007).

"Population aging will have dramatic effects on social entitlement programs, labor supply, trade, and savings around the globe and may demand new...approaches to accommodate a changing world" (NIA, 2007, p. 3). Global education about aging—which can inform policy, planning, service design, decision-making, social roles and norms, and family adaptations—is certainly one promising strategy for effectively accommodating the changing world.

Global education about aging includes two related but distinct kinds of initiatives: (a) developing gerontology programs within many nations around the world and (b) teaching about global aging within gerontology programs. This latter strategy can include infusion of comparative content into curriculum and/or an international study component. These two strategies for internationalizing gerontology—developing gerontology programs around the world and adding global content within programs—are discussed in the following sections.

GROWTH OF GERONTOLOGY EDUCATION
AROUND THE WORLD

Building and transmitting scientific knowledge about the processes of aging, about societal responses to dramatic demographic shifts, and about the individual and interpersonal implications of aging is crucial for effective planning for our aging populations. These knowledge-building and dissemination tasks are the role of gerontology education and research. Gerontology courses and programs take different directions in different cultural contexts. In many nations around the world, geriatric education is much more fully developed than gerontology, reflecting the priority given to the health care needs of the aging population. Interestingly, the United States has a great many gerontology programs, but the need for trained geriatricians is increasing at a much faster pace than the number of medical students graduating with that specialization.

Some efforts at gerontology education focus on adding gerontology content to professional credentials such as social work or medicine; other universities have interdisciplinary programs that emphasize research and the broad goals of liberal education; and still others focus on training a workforce. China, which is well-immersed in developing a system of gerontology education, now offers one of the few doctoral programs outside the United States, but gerontology content in China still tends to be incorporated into the curriculum of existing disciplines and professions (Wu, 2005).

In addition to diversity of the niches the programs seek to fill, gerontology education around the world varies by structure of the educational system, level of credentials, diverse nomenclature, and perspectives on who is a gerontologist (Guttman, 2007). Programs of study in gerontology vary according to the educational system within which it is housed, substantive focus, goals of the program, credentials offered, and specific societal needs the program seeks to meet. A complete inventory or comparative analysis of gerontology and geriatrics education programs in each nation is beyond the scope of this chapter, and there are no systematic data to support the task. However, a few examples will help to illustrate the variation in scope, purpose, and focus of programs in different parts of the world. It is certainly problematic to exclude vast regions and multiple nations around the world; a more complete inventory and description of all gerontology programs around the world is an important goal for the field.

United States
Gerontology education in the United States is well-established and widespread. The first gerontology courses began to be offered in the United States in the early 1960s. The most recent national directory compiled by the Association for Gerontology in Higher Education lists 774 programs from 354 institutions (Stepp, 2000) in the United States. In addition to associates degrees, and gerontology specialties within professional degrees such as social work and medicine, there are currently more than 200 bachelor's level programs, more than

150 master's degree programs, and 9 doctoral programs in gerontology in the United States. The number and focus of gerontology programs in the United States is always in flux, as the field responds to a dynamic range of opportunities and threats. The opportunities include a strong national awareness of the importance of aging and a well-developed system of services and products for older adults. In many U.S. schools, gerontology education has claimed its place as a discipline with its own theory and methods. However, students at the undergraduate and master's level who seek degrees that will prepare them for specific kinds of jobs sometimes choose professional training (such as social work) over a liberal education–based gerontology degree, even if the gerontology program is applied in focus and includes significant field experience. To shore up the viability of gerontology education, a growing number of U.S. gerontologists are calling for licensure or some other marketable credential or for "incorporating gerontology into legislation concerning requirements for practice" (Haley & Zelinski, 2007, p. 25).

Gerontology holds a strong position as a field of study relevant to having well-educated citizens prepared to deal with our aging society, and, at the graduate level, the field provides solid research training. The major threat to gerontology education is the competition against degrees that carry licensure or credentials that provide more immediate entrée into jobs and careers.

While gerontology education in the United States continues to solidify its position as a rigorous research and theory-based discipline, successful resolution of the credentialing issue will be essential for the field to thrive within its unique niche. Focus on outcomes, including number of grads and job placements; importance of clear niche and clear goals for program; as well as market and feasibility studies remains crucial.

Israel

Responding to the challenges of an aging society, Israel developed two graduate programs in gerontology in 1999. Together, the programs seek to expand the human capital necessary to support a growing service network, "mainly at the academic and research fronts, but also in top leadership management and care roles" (Carmel & Lowenstein, 2007, p. 50). As described by Carmel and Lowenstein (2007), each of the two graduate programs was created very intentionally to meet specific needs and target particular groups; one university has a program for physicians, and the other has a unique curriculum for case managers. Taken together, these two programs provide comprehensive, multidisciplinary, and high-quality training for professionals in a wide variety of fields, including medicine, allied health, law, behavioral sciences, and administration.

Japan

As noted previously, Japan currently holds a very unique demographic position: it is one of the oldest countries in the world (with very high life expectancy), and the proportion of its population 65 and over has transformed (from 7% to 14%) in a very short time (26 years). Japan's population age markers are similar to those of Western Europe, but it has made the transition to an aging society at the very rapid pace that is more commonly seen in developing nations.

Japan has very well-developed research infrastructures for gerontology and geriatrics, including professional societies and a growing number of scholarly journals. But higher education in gerontology is less well-developed. There are gerontology courses at several universities at both graduate and undergraduate levels, and courses on social welfare for older people are required for social work programs. But there are currently no undergraduate programs leading to a gerontology degree. One university (Obirin University Graduate School of International Studies) offers a master's degree and has recently started a doctoral degree in gerontology (Tsukada & Tatara, 2005). Along with a thorough description of gerontology research and education in Japan, Tsukada and Tatara provide thoughtful speculation about the slow pace of gerontology program development in a country that is so thoroughly immersed in issues of population aging. They cite a decision-making structure that involves several major government agencies with different priorities, and the lack of a national organization comparable the AGHE in the United States to promote higher education about aging. These authors suggest that grassroots efforts by faculty will be invaluable for gerontology higher education to progress in Japan (Tsukada & Tatara, 2005).

European Union

A number of countries in the European Union have formal graduate training in gerontology, including the University of Salamanca in Spain and Heidelberg University in Germany. The history, purpose, and substantive focus of programs in Spain, Finland, and the United Kingdom are summarized in a recent article by Askham, Gilhooly, Parketti, & Vega (2007), as are crucial issues of resource constraints, sustainability, and the debate over generalist versus specialist approaches to gerontology education.

In addition to programs within the traditional university structures, the EU has several postgraduate programs in gerontology that are unique in structure and implementation (van Rijsselt, Parkatti, & Troisi, 2007). One example from this category is the European Masters in Gerontology (EuMaG), which has a centralized administration (at Vrije University in Amsterdam), but courses are offered at multiple campuses throughout the academic year. Sometimes termed a carousel model, this program exposes students and faculty to diverse contexts and diverse approaches to the study of aging. EuMaG is a flexible program that is a joint venture of 22 universities and is designed to meet the needs of working professionals as well as traditional graduate students (van Rijsselt et al., 2007).

Kenya

The tremendous diversity among the many nations of the African continent make it impossible to summarize gerontology education and research efforts there, even though many African nations face similar population challenges. King, Gachui, Ice, Cattell, and Whittington (2005) note three aging-related issues shared by many African countries: marginalization of older adults without adequate informal support; the impact of HIV/AIDS on family structures and the obligations of grandparents; and highly vulnerable health and social security systems (p. 119).

Kenyatta University has a partnership with Georgia State University to develop a shared research agenda and to design one of Africa's few gerontology programs. The diploma program includes a rich array of gerontology courses (including research methods, family and aging, population, communication with older people, health, rural aging, psychology of aging, gender and aging, and creativity and aging); the idea for the program is very well-received among potential students and faculty and will, like any other program, depend on university resources for its implementation and success (King et al., 2005).

The arrangement between Kenyatta University and their U.S. partners involves the development of an academic program, a collaborative research agenda, faculty exchanges, and international research and educational opportunities for students. This partnership is a mutually beneficial arrangement that well illustrates another important aspect of the internationalization of gerontology: the value of incorporating cross-national content and experiences into gerontology research education.

NEED FOR CROSS-NATIONAL PERSPECTIVES WITHIN GERONTOLOGY EDUCATION

The value of international education experiences for students—in various forms, and for students from all disciplines—has received increasing emphasis in higher education. The Association of International Educators recently argued that study abroad is a "public good," citing the variety of crucial learning objectives that can best be achieved in international education: foreign language skills, cross-cultural understanding, and "an appreciation of a diverse and interconnected world" (NAFSA, 2008, p. 1).

Gerontology education is enhanced by international study in very specific ways. For those interested in helping students to understand the ways in which the experiences of aging are socially, historically, culturally, and economically influenced, a cross-cultural or international comparative perspective is invaluable. One could argue that it is difficult to discuss aging without using some kind of comparative perspective. Cross-cultural understanding surely reinforces messages about the ways in which social policies, caregiving systems, health care, and even health status are profoundly influenced by social and cultural context.

While we do not currently have systematic data on the prevalence of international education in gerontology, the increasing value placed on international education in all disciplines is reflected in significant growth in the number of students studying abroad—from 84,000 to 220,000 in the past decade (NAFSA 2008). This growth is significant, but the pace of increase is not quite as rapid as that projected by the Lincoln Commission as part of their vision for 1 million Americans studying abroad by the 2016–2017 academic year (Commission on the Abraham Lincoln Study Abroad Fellowship Program, 2005). The steady growth reflects commitment to the goals of international educational experiences; the slower than projected increase very likely reflects the significant challenges associated with study abroad programs, as discussed later in this chapter.

MODELS FOR INTERNATIONAL EDUCATION ABOUT AGING

While study abroad is seen by many as the most effective way to support students in their intercultural development, language skills, and broadened perspective on the subject matter they are studying, this opportunity is not feasible for every student. Seeking to balance the goals of study abroad with some of these significant challenges, gerontology, along with many other disciplines, has developed a range of alternatives for enhancing students' knowledge of aging in global context. A comparative perspective can be integrated into gerontology education by the intentional recruitment of students from diverse national backgrounds into a gerontology program or course, and by structuring assignments and discussions to highlight each student's informed perspective about aging in their home country. Two formal ways of internationalizing the gerontology curriculum are: through infusion of global aging content into existing curriculum and through various kinds of study abroad programs. Courses, workshops, and special programs for cross-national study of aging have increased in number and visibility over the past decade. Each of these strategies for teaching about the social and cultural contexts of aging has advantages, disadvantages, and variable levels of feasibility.

Curriculum Infusion

Incorporating global aging content into gerontology courses and developing courses on the topic of global aging are both becoming more prevalent in gerontology programs. This approach to globalizing the gerontology curriculum requires fewer administrative, financial, and institutional resources than study abroad programs. However, altering a curriculum in support of an international focus does require an intentional plan, faculty resources, and a rigorous approach to developing and implementing a comparative framework that is analytically sound and conceptually grounded.

A recent book edited by Shenk and Groger (2005) describes several examples of course development and teaching strategies for incorporating cross-cultural perspectives into gerontology curricula. Authors in this volume describe teaching approaches that incorporate film, literature, and religion to illustrate the importance of culture in shaping the experiences of aging. Elliott (2005) describes an aging services course in which she helps students develop greater awareness of cultural differences among elders (within the United States); from that standpoint, they are encouraged to critique standardized assessment techniques for their insensitivity to salient and significant cultural differences that can have great impact on service delivery preferences, such as expectations about family caregiving.

The examples in Shenk and Groger are based in a wide range of disciplines, including humanities, anthropology, sociology, social welfare, and gerontology. This diversity speaks to the richness and broad possibilities of a comparative approach to gerontology. The multiple disciplines that can contribute to the infusion of global aging into gerontology programs also reinforces the necessity of fitting a well-developed and rigorous comparative approach to the overall perspective of the program and expertise of the faculty. An anthropological approach to the comparative study of informal caregiving systems in different cultures, for example, would necessarily be different from a policy-based comparative analysis of health care systems, and would require different analytical frameworks. Even within a particular, discipline-specific comparative framework, description of differences can only advance an internationalizing agenda so far. For example, knowing about the different pension systems in the United States and Germany typically engages students' curiosity, but understanding the ways in which ideology, history, cultural values, and policy processes helped to shape those very different pension systems would take students much further in their cross-cultural, international study of global aging. Perhaps the most important message implicit in the Shenk and Groger volume is that including information about aging in different contexts is only the starting point for helping students to develop a rigorous, analytical perspective on the role of social and cultural factors in shaping the experiences of and societal responses to aging.

Study Abroad

Studying in a country other than one's own provides students with opportunities beyond what is possible even in the best comparative gerontology course. The first-hand experiences of another culture, getting to meet and know older people in their own homes in a setting different from the student's own familiar surroundings, and being able to observe and analyze social and health service systems that look and operate very differently from those at home, are invaluable. The far-reaching benefits of a study abroad experience are, to at least some degree, matched by the resources required to establish and maintain high quality. These resources include costs to the students; costs to the university in the form of international education and admissions office staff time; and faculty time to structure, advise, and supervise learning experiences. And the logistics of study abroad are extensive. In addition, assessing and assuring the quality of the educational program is a considerable challenges (van Rijsselt et al., 2007).

These issues of costs, accessibility, logistics, and quality are common to all kinds of study abroad programs. But there are different kinds of study abroad programs, each with disadvantages and advantages. Two kinds of programs for the comparative study of aging in different countries, here termed *immersion* and *guided study,* vary by length, language requirements, resource requirements, and role of home and host institution faculty.

Immersion Programs

This model focuses on depth of international learning experience, and is probably best exemplified by an exchange program or a semester-long study abroad. Students typically spend at least one semester at their host institution; faculty and administration at both the sending and receiving institutions have a high level of involvement with the program. Support from university administrators (including International Education Officers and their staff and admissions officers) is essential for the success of such programs, as is the guidance of faculty and staff in the gerontology program at the receiving institution. Communication between gerontology faculty at home and host institutions is essential for assuring the quality of the learning experience. Students are usually required to have or to develop proficiency in the language of the host country adequate to succeed in classroom learning. The logistics of setting up a student exchange and/or semester abroad are significant and often require a fair amount of independence and perseverance on the part of the student. Arranging for visas, housing, and transportation are a few of the logistics that require attention from program faculty and the student.

Several U.S. and EU institutions of higher education have established an exchange program for the comparative study of social and health policy for aging societies. Funded by the U.S. Department of Education, Fund for the Improvement of Postsecondary Education, and the EU Directorate for Education and Culture, this program, called Intergero (shorthand for International Interdisciplinary Program in Gerontology), well illustrates the value of exchange programs in gerontology. In spite of some occasional logistical challenges, data from students who have participated in the program have unequivocally praised the opportunity—students cite their personal growth, the depth of the substantive learning they gained, and the international network of colleagues that they developed as a result of the immersion in another culture. Faculty who have had the exchange students in their programs have also evaluated the program very highly, citing the invaluable information and perspectives brought to the classroom by the international students. One U.S. faculty member stated that he will never teach his social policy and aging class the same way because of all he and the students have learned from the cross-cultural comparative analyses enabled by having international students in the class.

Guided Study

While the benefits of an exchange program or semester abroad are undeniable, this option is less feasible for many students. For some gerontology programs, it may not be the best option for globalizing the curriculum. Several universities have implemented guided study programs: shorter-term experiences for groups of students, typically led by a faculty member from the students' home institution. The language requirements are usually not as extensive as for an immersion program, because courses in a guided study model are typically taught in the students' home-institution language. These programs do require a great deal of planning and coordination, often blending classroom and extramural learning. A good partnership with at least one institution in the receiving country is necessary for smooth planning of the curriculum and the outside-the-classroom experiences. While the immersion model emphasizes depth of cultural experience, the guided study model usually places great emphasis on breadth, sometimes building in experiences in more than one culture.

Based on data presented at meetings of the Gerontological Society of America and the AGHE, student learning outcomes from guided international study programs are very positive—a broader perspective on the role of social and cultural forces in shaping the experiences of aging and the varying approaches to the design and provision of services for older adults. There is arguably less intercultural development for students in guided study versus immersion programs. Students who show the greatest intercultural development spend moderate amounts of time with host families (or host country students), and moderate amounts of time with other U.S. students. Those who spend most of their time with other U.S. students, and those who are completely immersed, did not improve as much in intercultural growth (NAFSA, 2008).

The choice to add an international study abroad experience, and which approach to adopt, clearly depends on balancing breadth versus depth priorities for the program, nature of relationships with universities outside the United States, students served by the university, and decisions about the language requirements and the administrative and financial resources required and available.

SUMMARY

"Population aging is unprecedented, pervasive, enduring, and has profound implications for most facets of human life" (UN, 2002, p. xxviii). This eloquent description of the enormous changes we face is the foundation of the international mandate for gerontology education. In order to meet the opportunities and challenges that accompany population aging, gerontology education is essential. The growth of gerontology programs around the world, and the internationalization of gerontology programs, speak to the value of education about global aging, and to the value of cross-cultural collaborations on education and research about aging. Global and globalized gerontology education can position us to adapt to and plan for our aging populations, giving credence to a paraphrase of Aristotle's advice: international education is the best provision for old age.

REFERENCES

Askham, J., Gilhooly, M., Parketti, T., & Vega, J. (2007). Speculations on the future of taught masters courses in gerontology: Lessons from a comparison of England, Scotland, Finland, and Spain. *Gerontology and Geriatrics Education, 27*(3), 27–47.

58   ANNUAL REVIEW OF GERONTOLOGY AND GERIATRICS

Butler, R. (2008). *The longevity revolution: The benefits and challenges of living a long life.* New York: Perseus Publishing.

Carmel, S., & Lowenstein, A. (2007). Addressing a nation's challenge: Graduate programs in gerontology in Israel. *Gerontology and Geriatrics Education, 27*(3), 49–63.

Commission on the Abraham Lincoln Study Abroad Fellowship Program. (2005). *Global competence and national needs.* Retrieved from http://www.nafsa.org/_/Document/_/lincoln_commission_report.pdf

Elliott, K. (2005). Course design on aging: Incorporating cross-cultural perspectives that challenge assumptions about assessment and service delivery. In D. Shenk & L. Groger (Eds.), *Aging education in a global context* (pp. 23–42). New York: Haworth Press.

Guttman, G. (2007). IAGG's role in graduate education in gerontology. *Gerontology and Geriatrics Education, 27*(3), 1–10.

Haley, W., & Zelinski, E. (2007). Progress and challenges in graduate education: The U.S. experience. *Gerontology and Geriatrics Education, 27*(7), 11–26.

King, S., Gachui, M., Ice, G., Cattell, M., & Whittington, F. (2005). Gerontology education and research in Kenya: Establishing a US-African partnership in aging. In D. Shenk & L. Groger (Eds.), *Aging education in a global context* (pp. 117–136). New York: Haworth Press.

Kinsella, D., & Phillips, D. (2005). Global aging: The challenge of success. *Population Bulletin, 60*(1). Washington, DC: Population Reference Bureau.

Laertius, Diogenes. *Lives of eminent philosophers: Aristotle* (trans. C. D. Young). Retrieved May 1, 2008, from http://classicpersuasion.org/pw/diogenes/dlaristotle.htm

NAFSA: Association of International Educators. (2008). *Strengthening study abroad: Recommendations for effective institutional management for presidents, senior administrators, and study abroad professionals.* Retrieved October 1, 2008, from http://www.nafsa.org/IMSA

National Institute on Aging. (2007). *Why population aging matters: A global perspective.* Retrieved October 15, 2008, from http://www.state.gov/documents/organization/81775.pdf

Shenk, D., & Groger, L. (Eds.). (2005). *Aging education in a global context.* New York: Haworth Press.

Stepp, D. (Ed). (2000). *Directory of educational programs in gerontology and geriatrics* (7th ed.). Washington, DC: Association for Gerontology in Higher Education.

Tsukada, N., & Tatara, T. (2005). Gerontology programs in Japanese higher education. In D. Shenk & L. Groger (Eds.), *Aging education in a global context* (pp. 97–116). New York: Haworth Press.

United Nations, Department of Economic and Social Affairs, Population Division. (2002). *World population ageing: 1950–2050.* New York: Author.

van Rijsselt, R., Parkatti, T., & Troisi, J. (2007). European initiatives in postgraduate education in gerontology. *Gerontology and Geriatrics Education, 27*(3), 79–97.

Wu, B. (2005). Teaching Chinese health care professionals about community-based long-term care in China. In D. Shenk & L. Groger (Eds.), *Aging education in a global context* (pp. 137–150). New York: Haworth Press.

SECTION II

ETHICS AND CULTURAL
ISSUES IN GERONTOLOGY

This section focuses on specific areas of gerontology education and the education of adults and older adults including the need to develop sensitivity to key education issues related to ethics, social policy, cultural diversity, and lifelong learning. This section opens with a chapter by Marshall B. Kapp of Southern Illinois University titled "Ethics Education in Gerontology and Geriatrics" and focuses the education about ethical issues in the planning, delivery, and evaluation of gerontological and geriatric care. Empathy, sensitivity, and compassion need to be cultivated, and education needs to employ them in analyzing and resolving ethical dilemmas. Numerous approaches and resources are recommended.

The next chapter is by Robert H. Binstock of Case Western Reserve University and is titled "Social Policy in Gerontology and Geriatrics Education." He presents the importance of education about social policy for students in gerontology and geriatrics. Analysis of current policies, history of policy development, and new approaches to social policy are central components of professional and general education. Resources for course development and course activities are presented. Examples of the evolution and consequences of gerontological research and public policy are reviewed.

The third chapter is by Gwen Yeo and Melen McBride of Stanford University and is titled "Cultural Diversity in Geriatrics and Gerontology Education." It focuses on education to prepare students to serve an increasingly heterogeneous population of older adults. Emphasis is placed on the unique needs and issues associated with each cultural group. This chapter reviews the development of ethnogerontology and ethnogeriatrics and shows how curriculum has been developed to prepare students to work with culturally diverse populations of older adults. Resources including curriculum, modules, articles, Web sites and media are presented.

Ronald J. Manheimer of The University of North Carolina at Asheville concludes this section with a discussion of lifelong learning titled "Lifelong Learning in Aging Societies: Emerging Paradigms." He reviews the history and development of learning opportunities for adults and older adults. Gerontological research supports the importance of fostering continued intellectual, emotional, and spiritual development. This includes continuing education related to both work and leisure. Global approaches to older adult learning provide many strong models. Exemplary programs in a variety of settings are reviewed.

CHAPTER 5

Ethics Education in Gerontology and Geriatrics

Marshall B. Kapp

Caring for older persons is a significant part of current professional life for providers of health care, human, and business services in the United States. The older individual living in a complex modern society often confronts an array of life challenges that necessitate the invocation of professional assistance. Planning, delivering, and evaluating gerontological and geriatric care implicates a wide variety of ethical issues for various kinds of practitioners and for those who advocate for, develop, and implement the public policies within which products and services for the aged are provided. Consequently, one would expect educators of present and future service and public policy professionals in the aging sphere to integrate a substantial amount of teaching about ethical issues into the course content for those professionals, and indeed we have begun to witness at least some substantial movement in this direction over the past couple of decades in undergraduate, graduate, and continuing professional education programs aimed at these student audiences (Moody & Mangum, 2004).

RATIONALE

Aside from the obvious national and global demographic trend entailing a rapidly increasing number and percentage of older citizens (particularly in the fastest-growing category of "old old"), at least two other factors dictate

DOI: 10.1891/0198-8794.28.61

the need for particularized attention in gerontological/geriatric education to ethical problems facing older patients/clients. First, this sphere implicates a distinct body of knowledge and skills; many ethical issues either are unique to older persons or, if generic in nature, affect the elderly in different ways. Thus, generic ethics coursework alone is not sufficient. Second, the role of the gerontologically educated individual as both clinical caregiver and advocate for the total well-being of the patient/client takes on added significance when older patients/clients are involved. Focused educational endeavors are essential to preparing future health care, human, and business services professionals to fulfill this dual role on behalf of the older patients/clients for whom they both care and advocate.

In general terms, cognitive knowledge of both the process of ethical reasoning and the substantive ethical principles applicable to gerontological practice is essential for the modern health care, human services, and business professional. Ethics touch all human activities, including those encompassed within gerontological practice. Ethics help define the nature, extent, and limits of the rights and obligations emerging from the relationships between gerontological professionals, patients/clients, families, facilities, third-party payers and reviewers, and society. In addition to its direct impact on the permissible or desirable boundaries of clinical and management decisions and actions, ethics also affect gerontological practice by drawing the professional into the social problems or disputes of the patient/client that require fair and just resolution.

Beyond these reasons, ethics instruction properly performed can instill in the developing gerontologist a greater sense of empathy and compassion toward patients/clients and professional colleagues. Stated differently, it can contribute to the humanization of aging services. Exposure to ethical principles and reasoning can exert a salutary influence over the whole professionalization process and, more significantly, over the future everyday behavior of health and human services and business students toward their older patients/clients, family members of those patients/clients, and their colleagues. Criticisms of the dehumanizing effects on current students of the grueling, increasingly technical process of professional education abound, as do calls for educational reforms to instill the future caregiver with a greater degree of compassion and sensitivity. Infusion of ethical ideals and thinking can contribute significantly to such reforms. Ethical education of health and human services professionals can be a valuable tool for patient/client advocacy, for it can encourage forms of caring that respect dignity and improve lives, especially for disadvantaged and/or vulnerable population groups such as the elderly or the chronically mentally ill.

For example, more than a quarter century ago the President's Commission for the Study of Ethical Problems in Medicine and Biomedical and Behavioral Research commented (in the context of discussing informed consent):

> Since the Commission believes that physicians are responsible for ensuring that patients can participate as much as possible in decisions about their care, medical educators ought to train students to carry out this obligation. Such education and training should not only equip students with necessary communications skills, but also lead them to value the patient as a full participant in medical decision making. (President's Commission, 1982, p. 143)

Instruction in ethics and its underlying precepts can play a vital role in fulfilling the spirit of the Commission's recommendation. Additionally, it can affect the totality not only of medical practice, but the provision of health care, human services, and business generally and geriatric and gerontological services particularly.

There is more than idealism at play here, though. In practical terms, an understanding of the kinds of obligations and limitations that ethics place on gerontological practice provides the practitioner with a distinct pragmatic advantage in minimizing exposure to possible criminal or civil liability. Without this background, the caregiving professional is more likely to commit unknowing and avoidable violations of criminal restrictions and civil duties owed to other individuals and entities.

Thus, the ultimate goals of ethics education in the aging arena are twofold (Rooksby, 2007). One goal is to create virtuous health care, human services, and business professionals who will interact ethically with and assist older persons. The second goal is to use education to provide future and present geriatric and gerontological professionals with a specialized skill set to employ in analyzing and resolving ethical dilemmas.

ACTORS

Who is best qualified to successfully integrate ethical issues into the aging curriculum? Certainly, this responsibility should be included in the job descriptions of philosophers and attorneys, as well as faculty with graduate degrees specifically in bioethics (American Society for Bioethics and Humanities, 2008), who hold full or part-time academic appointments in schools of health care, human services, and business professions. Where an institution educating health and human services professionals has not yet added someone with such an academic background to its faculty, borrowing persons with the requisite expertise and experience from neighboring academic programs in the humanities and social sciences should be explored. Practicing attorneys and ethics consultants, including appropriately educated clergy or chaplains, from the surrounding community may perform a useful service by volunteering to share their time and experience in appropriate educational settings. Professional advocates for older persons can function as significant agents in positively altering health care and human services providers' perceptions and conduct.

For all of these potential educators, the importance of enthusiastic cooperation and collaboration with actively practicing clinicians and policy makers cannot be overemphasized. Health care, human services, and business professionals understandably tend to identify with, and assign role model status to, similar professionals rather than philosophers, attorneys, or members of other, seemingly foreign professions. To the extent that the philosopher, attorney, advocate, or other faculty member is able to enlist the visible and genuine support of respected hands-on health care, human services, and business practitioners, from within both the academic institution and the local community, in publicly discussing ethical issues arising in geriatric and gerontological care, the receptivity of the student audience to the lessons being taught will rise appreciably. Taking care of older individuals often requires a multidisciplinary, interdisciplinary team effort (Anetzberger, 2007), and gerontology's multidisciplinary and interdisciplinary nature should be reflected in the composition and staffing of educational programs.

Successful educators in this sphere need to have certain specific qualities. First and most obviously, a sufficient degree of meaningful expertise and experience in the subject area must be demonstrated. In addition, the educator needs to display an aura of responsibility, maturity, and good judgment. Students will resist educational overtures from those whom they perceive, accurately or not, as angry, self-righteous moral complainers intent only on chastising, hectoring, and demagoguery. Finally, educators must be, in both appearance and fact, sufficiently grounded in the real world of geriatric and gerontological service and delivery. Health care, human services, and business professionals and students are, as a general matter, rather pragmatically, tangibly oriented, and they tend to be interested in conceptual analysis only to the degree that theory can be translated directly into explicit guidelines that can be made applicable to everyday clinical practice. While never deviating from their chief role as advocate for older patients/clients, ethical and legal educators must endeavor to demonstrate an understanding of—and an empathy for—the realties encountered by health care, human services, and business professionals on a daily basis; otherwise their attempted message is likely to be rejected as a purely intellectual exercise.

CONTEXTS

What are the most appropriate contexts for integrating ethical (as well as related social, financial, and legal) issues into geriatric and gerontological education? Put differently, where should ethics education concerning older persons take place, and in what forms? Students are a highly impressionable group, and therefore the "medium" (including the time and place) of activity is definitely part of the message they are most likely to receive (McLuhan & Fiore, 1967).

Undergraduate premedical programs, as well as undergraduate, graduate, and postgraduate educational programs in nursing, psychology, social work, the allied health professions, business, and public policy are all likely candidates for efforts to integrate ethical content regarding aging and older people. Law schools represent a particularly fertile avenue for such integration, with opportunities existing across many parts of the entire curriculum (Morgan, 2001) but especially in specific courses (required for every student in every American law school under current American Bar Association accreditation standards) on professional responsibility, wherein students learn how to interpret and apply provisions of the American Bar Association (ABA) Model Rules of Conduct (Longan, 2001), plus elective elder law courses (Elder Law Course Survey, 2007).

Regarding medical education specifically, there are several logical sites. Individual medical and osteopathic schools are the most immediate target. Officials at medical and osteopathic schools with curricular authority should be cultivated and lobbied. Moreover, educational activities in ethics and aging should take place within local health care institutions and agencies (including hospitals, nursing homes, assisted-living facilities, hospices, adult day care centers, and home health agencies) that are affiliated with the medical school for the purpose of offering medical students and postgraduate trainees (i.e., medical residents) hands-on exposure to caring for the elderly. Local, state, and in certain cases even national general and specialty medical associations that conduct meetings and sponsor conferences and programs with substantive geriatric content should also be considered prime opportunities for the productive integration of ethics teaching.

There are many forms that integration of ethical issues into the overall geriatric and gerontological curriculum might take. One choice certainly is formal instruction. This could be carried out as part of a larger core course or conducted separately on a required or an elective basis. Format could be lecture, seminar, or a combination of the two. Additionally, student clinical placements involving opportunities for exposure to, and on the ground involvement in, the kinds of real life ethical conundrums (Kane & Caplan, 1990) with which professionals and organizations serving older patients/clients and their families are confronted on a regular basis need to be extensively explored.

Linkages should be developed among health care, human services, and business professional schools, health care facilities and agencies, human services agencies providing services to the older population, senior citizen advocacy organizations, financial services firms, and businesses to provide possibilities for the sponsorship and supervision of students as observers, interns, or externs (Kapp, 2000).

Moreover, attention to ethical issues may be integrated into departmental case conferences, grand rounds, and special lectures (either independently organized or invited as part of an already established course or meeting schedule) to audiences made up—in whole or part—of students with an interest in geriatrics and gerontology. Further, educational institutions in the business of training future professionals who will encounter older patients/clients in their practices are frequently on the alert for qualified preceptors with whom to pair students in individual tutorials, and many people involved in the ethics of aging could take on that role successfully. Also, formal continuing education programs and informal brown bag lunches, scheduled regularly or irregularly at strategic sites, are examples of other possible forums to be explored.

An important related pedagogical issue is that of proper timing. There is great virtue in endeavoring to reach the fledgling gerontological professional very early in the formal professionalization and socialization process, while he or she is still more of a "civilian" than a seasoned professional. Appropriate learning experiences at the incipient stages of career development are likely to bear fruit in sensitizing individuals to significant issues, concepts, arguments, and processes, establishing attitudes of tolerance and open-mindedness, and building the desire and foundation for the life-long acquisition of additional skills and knowledge.

However, learning ethical principles and reasoning processes (Dubler & Liebman, 2004) is, as is true for many other facets of professional development, a slow and incremental process. Basic principles introduced early require constant reinforcement, clarification, and expansion throughout the student's academic journey, especially in conjunction with its experiential components. Even though students are given the chance to apply ethical principles and processes in carrying out their professional mandates, they will be unable, without some theoretical background instruction, to integrate the particular ethical lessons into a useful framework for practice.

Besides the detail of when ethics education should occur, there is the mundane but essential question of where it ought to take place. The physical location matters a great deal. The usual campus auditorium or classroom is often unavoidable and is quite reasonably suited to its purpose. As health care and human services students mature clinically, though, they seem to attach greater weight to messages delivered in health care facility and agency conference rooms (even if the words actually uttered are no different than those exchanged within the confines of a campus classroom). Thus, opportunities for on-site teaching opportunities should be assiduously pursued.

APPROACHES

Once suitable teaching contexts have been selected and secured, the temptation to resort to the legal model, under which instructors attempt to frighten students into learning and obeying a rigid set of so-called black letter rules, lest they be exposed to punitive actions in the form of lawsuits, professional disciplinary sanctions, or even criminal prosecutions, should be resisted strenuously. Such an approach inevitably tends to engender negative feelings and misperceptions about the character of both ethics and law. Instead, there must be concentration on a much broader process and value-focused presentation of the subject matter. Otherwise, the student audience is likely to develop the attitude (or, more likely the preexisting attitude will be reinforced) that ethics and law are mainly an obstruction in their lives rather than a valuable source of guidance in their work.

CONTENT

Ethics as a field of study is multifaceted (Johnson, 1999). Metaethics is the subdivision centering on raising questions about conceptualizations in the domain of ethics; in other words, metaethics is the discipline that explores how we decide what is an ethical issue. Ideology, the second branch of ethics, encompasses the ethical theories that have been systematically constructed to make judgments of right conduct and to explicitly or implicitly state beliefs that are wrong; this branch provides the criteria for a normative system that analyzes right and wrong.

The third branch of ethics—and definitely the one most relevant to the geriatric and gerontological educational endeavors being discussed in this essay—is termed applied ethics. In this form, ideological or theoretical constructs (most importantly in the gerontological sphere, the ethical principles of autonomy, respect, privacy, beneficence, nonmaleficence or doing no harm, justice, fidelity, and veracity) are brought to bear on particular, concrete life situations. This is where we move from the study, for its own sake, of ethics as a conceptual phenomenon to direct attention to actually using ethical principles to resolve questions in the practice, research, or policy settings.

Put in somewhat different terms, the President's Council on Bioethics (2005, p. 110) described "the ethics of caregiving" as follows:

> To think about *ethics* is to think about the goals we pursue for ourselves and others (the good); about the kind of actions we do (the right); and about the sort of people we hope to be (our character). Each of these aspects of ethics is important, and each makes its claim upon us.

Educators should adopt a flexible approach concerning the appropriate substantive content they intend to convey. The time and format available for student contact, as well as the immediate and long-term needs and interests of the specific audience, should be taken carefully into account. Basic but recurring ethical problems should not be ignored in favor of more trendy—and often, frankly, more intellectually interesting—subjects. Questions that many service providers and advocates for older persons might consider mundane, such as what information may be omitted from the individual's clinical record, are of critical importance to health care and human services professionals functioning daily in the trenches. Although situations arising within total residential institutions, such as nursing homes or public in-patient mental health facilities, are of serious concern, it is important also to address the many complex ethical questions that come to the fore in the community settings that are the main sites of most health care, human, and financial services delivered to older persons today. Finally, educators must strive to introduce into their concentration on practical, discrete issues involving particular professional/patient relationships a proper blending of such larger public policy issues relating to matters such as reform of the health care financing and delivery system/marketplace and changes in how we provide and pay for long-term care services to older persons. Immediate, pragmatic concerns and the larger societal picture are inextricably intertwined in practice, and should be treated similarly in the educational context.

Specific topics that might be covered as part of educational efforts in aging and ethics abound. A problem-oriented approach, for example, could focus students on such questions as: Who is my client (when the family is functioning as spokesperson, translator, and/or bill payer)? Who makes the decisions (for the impaired but not incompetent client or for the incompetent client with or without a guardian)? (Longan, 2001). These questions are generic, in the sense of challenging members of all the helping professions as they deal with older patients/clients.

RESOURCES

The topic of resources is best divided into two parts. First, what resources are available to support the educator involved in integrating ethical content into the geriatric and gerontological curriculum? Then, what resources should students be assigned to study as part of this educational endeavor?

For the ethics educator, the resource situation has improved markedly over the last three decades. A variety of private organizations (see Appendix A), journals/newsletters (Appendix B), and textbooks, in ethics and law (Frolik & Barnes, 2007; Dayton, Wood, & Belian, 2007) with at least a secondary if not primary emphasis on aging have surfaced to support the individual educator in developing and implementing worthwhile educational experiences in this arena. So, too, have organizations, journals, and textbooks on aging that include at least a secondary interest in ethical and legal matters (Kapp, 2004). A number of sample course syllabi in ethics and aging are publicly available (Appendix B).

The question of outside reading assignments for students in connection with ethics teaching activities is a difficult one. In my own teaching experience, the expectation that many health care and human services students who are already frequently overwhelmed by the rest of their academic workload will devote sufficient time and energy to closely read, let alone intellectually digest, complicated primary ethics materials (i.e., books and articles written by professional philosophers for consumption by other scholars in their own discipline and published in specialty philosophy or ethics outlets) or legal materials (i.e., bills, statutes, regulations, executive orders, and judicial opinions) or legal textbooks or law review literature is quite unrealistic. Instead, textbooks and journal articles describing and illustrating ethical—(and related legal (Kapp, in preparation 2009)—and social) concepts that have been created consciously and explicitly for health care and human services audiences are more likely to be willingly and usefully swallowed and digested by students and practitioners in those professions.

Moreover, ethical (as well as legal and public policy) issues are covered regularly and extensively in the health care and human services literature (i.e., the students' own professional venues) and the public press. The assignment of appropriate—that is, ethically and legally accurate and sufficiently sophisticated but without undue reliance on obtuse philosophical and legal jargon—readings from prominent journals such as the *New England Journal of Medicine, Journal of the American Medical Association, Annals of Internal Medicine, and Archives of Internal Medicine,* and respected newspapers such as the *Wall Street Journal* will be perceived as more relevant and more comprehensible by health care, human services, and business students, and thus will serve a more valuable role in their education, than would be the case with ethical materials intended for philosophers or legal materials written by attorneys for their professional colleagues.

IMPEDIMENTS AND PROSPECTS

There are at least a couple of significant impediments to accomplishing the goals urged in this essay, most prominently curricular time constraints and academic professional biases. Direct teaching time access to students, postgraduate trainees, and practicing professionals is one of the most precious and jealously guarded commodities within the educational domain. Current departmental contestants who are already competing for that limited access often are not overly receptive to another set of actors with another set of claims on student time and attention. Beyond the issue of time limitations, existing political powers within academic institutions may, as a matter of their own professional training or bias, be disinclined or even actively antagonistic toward geriatric and gerontological education generally or to the integration of ethical (as well as legal and social) issues particularly.

A large-scale interprofessional campaign of information and persuasion needs to be carried out to secure adequate treatment in the allocation of scarce curriculum time and other resources and to reconcile with the key change agents in the academic political sphere. A major challenge is likely to be convincing resistant health care, human services, and business professionals that providing services to older citizens in a manner that protects and promotes clinical, social, and financial well-being for both provider and consumer absolutely must involve careful attention to the ethical aspects of service delivery, including those ethical aspects unique to older patients/clients.

CONCLUSION

The pedagogical justifications for integrating ethics-centered activities into geriatric and gerontological education are sound. Ethical precepts and processes, in the aging arena as elsewhere, generally are consistent with common sense, sound judgment, and clinically acceptable practice. Ethics must be converted from a mysterious collection of externally announced prescriptions and proscriptions into an understandable body of sensible and humane guidelines for action.

Effective venues and methods can be developed and perfected, logistical details can be negotiated, and competent faculty can be identified and trained. The potential curricular content is rich and rigorous. As health care, human services, and business professionals come into contact with older persons with growing frequency, it is essential that this contact be as positive and productive as possible, not only for the professional's own ethical, legal, financial, and emotional health, but also for the ultimate welfare of the older patients/clients and their families whom all of these professions, after all, exist to serve.

APPENDIX A

AARP Office of Academic Affairs, http://aarp.org/research/academic

American Bar Association Commission on Law and Aging, http://www.abanet.org/aging

American College of Legal Medicine, http://www.aclm.org

American Society for Bioethics and Humanities, http://www.asbh.org/meetings/resources/bioethics.html

American Society of Law, Medicine and Ethics, http://www.aslme.org

Association for Gerontology in Higher Education (AGHE), http://www.geron.org/

Hastings Center, http://www.thehastingscenter.org

Kennedy Institute of Ethics, Georgetown University, http://kennedyinstitute.georgetown.edu/

APPENDIX B

AgeSource Worldwide, http://www.aarp.org/research/agesource

American Journal of Bioethics, http://www.bioethics.net/journal

Bioethics Matters (Newsletter of the Hastings Center), http://www.thehastingscenter.org/bioethics-matters

BIFOCAL (Bar Associations in Focus on Aging and the Law), http://www.abanet.org/aging/publications/bifocal

Syllabus for Values, Decision Making, and Elderly course at Northeastern Illinois University, http://www.neiu.edu/~deptpsyc/426.htm

Syllabus for Aging and Ethical Issues course at University of Vermont, http://www.uvm.edu/~scutler/soc222/

Elder Law Journal, University of Illinois College of Law, http://elderlaw.law.uiuc.edu

Hastings Center Report, http://www.thehastingscenter.org/publications/hcr

Journal of Law, Medicine, and Ethics, http://www.aslme.org/pub

Kennedy Institute of Ethics Journal, http://kennedyinstitute.georgetown.edu/publications/kie_journal.htm

Teaching Gerontology Research Report, http://www.aarp.org/research/academic/teaching_gerontology.html

REFERENCES

American Society for Bioethics and Humanities. (2008). *Bioethics and humanities education—Masters and other programs*. Retrieved September 29, 2008, from http://www.asbh.org/meetings/resources/bioethics.html

Anetzberger, G. (2007). Responding to elder abuse: Interdisciplinary cooperation or leadership void? *Gerontologist, 47*(5), 711–715.

Dayton, A. K., Wood, M. M., & Belian, J. (2007). *Elder law: Readings, cases, and materials,* (3rd ed.). Newark, NJ: Matthew Bender & Company.

Dubler, N. N., & Liebman, C. B. (2004). *Bioethics mediation: A guide to shaping shared solutions.* New York: United Hospital Fund.

Elder Law Course Survey. (2007). Retrieved from http://www.law.stetson.edu/excellence/elderlaw/ElderLawCourseSurvey.pdf

Frolik, L. A., & Barnes, A. M. (2007). *Elder law: Cases and materials,* (4th ed.). Newark, NJ: Matthew Bender & Company.

Johnson, T. F., (Ed.). (1999). *Handbook on ethical issues on aging.* Westport, CT: Greenwood Press.

Kapp, M. B. (2000). Professional development in law, health care, and aging: A model fellowship program. *Gerontologist, 40*(3), 364–366.

Kapp, M. B. (2004). *Law and aging: A selected annotated bibliography for gerontology instruction.* Washington, DC: Association for Gerontology in Higher Education.

Kapp, M. B. (In preparation 2009). *Legal aspects of elder care.* Sudbury, MA: Jones and Bartlett Publishers.

Kane. R. A., & Caplan, A. L. (1990). *Everyday ethics: Resolving dilemmas in nursing home life.* New York: Springer Publishing Company.

Longan, P. E. (2001). Elder law across the curriculum: Professional responsibility. *Stetson Law Review, 30*(4), 1413–1426.

McLuhan, M., & Fiore, Q. (1967). *The medium is the message.* New York: Random House.

Messikomer, C. M., & Cirka, C. C. (2007). Managing everyday ethics in assisted living: A research-based case analysis for the classroom. *Gerontology and Geriatrics Education, 28*(4), 99–128.

Moody, H. R., & Mangum, W. P. (compilers). (2004). *Ethics and aging: A selected annotated bibliography for gerontology instruction.* Washington, DC: Association for Gerontology in Higher Education.

Morgan, R. C. (2001). Introduction to symposium on elder law across the curriculum. *Stetson Law Review, 30*(4), 1265–1272.

President's Commission for the Study of Ethical Problems in Medicine and Biomedical and Behavioral Research. (1982). *Making health care decisions: The ethical and legal implications of informed consent in the patient-practitioner relationship.* Washington, DC: Government Printing Office.

President's Council on Bioethics. (2005). *Taking care: Ethical caregiving in our aging society.* Washington, DC: Author. Retrieved from http://www.bioethics.gov

Rooksby, J. H. (2007). Ethics education in medical schools: Problems, practices, and possibilities. *Quinnipiac Health Law Journal, 10,* 181–217.

CHAPTER 6

Social Policy in Gerontology and Geriatrics Education

Robert H. Binstock

A gerontology or geriatrics curriculum that does not include social policy is missing essential ingredients for understanding the everyday situations of older individuals and how they come about, what may pose threats to them, and—when needed—how their situations might be changed for the better through new policies. Knowledge of social policy also illuminates relationships between older people and younger generations, a variety of social institutions, and the society at large.

As exemplified by the preceding paragraph, this discussion of social policy in gerontology and geriatrics education contains many assertions and opinions. Such observations are based on my ongoing experience in teaching social policy and aging for more than 40 years. My students have included various types of PhD, MD, and master's degree students, as well as undergraduates. Their backgrounds, concentrations, and majors have been in anthropology, bioethics, economics, gerontology, health services research, history, law, management, medicine, nursing, nutrition, political science, psychology, public health, social policy, social work, and sociology.

In this chapter I first briefly outline the superficial terrain of the potential scope of education in social policy and aging. Next, I suggest a variety

The author wishes to acknowledge Melissa Castora for reading a preliminary draft of this chapter and making helpful suggestions.

DOI: 10.1891/0198-8794.28.73

of educational resources for both students and teachers. In a final section I discuss selected concepts and perspectives that I have found useful in teaching aging and social policy. Policy examples provided in these discussions are drawn primarily from the United States because of space considerations. However, as indicated through brief allusions to policy experiences in other countries, cross-national comparisons can be valuable in social policy education.

THE POTENTIAL SCOPE OF EDUCATION IN SOCIAL POLICY AND AGING

Teaching social policy can include attention to a wide variety of existing policies in both the public and private sectors of society. It can also encompass analyses of current policy proposals, development of new ideas for policies, and study of the history of policies in order to understand how and why they became what they are.

The mention of *public* policies in the field of aging immediately brings to mind such major federal policies as Social Security, Medicare, and Medicaid, the Older Americans Act, the Age Discrimination in Employment Act, the Employee Retirement Income Security Act, and the establishment of a National Institute on Aging. But of course there are myriad other policies affecting aging and older persons at the federal and state levels, as well as the actions and inactions of municipal, county, and special district governments. Think, for instance, of nursing home fires and poor enforcement of city fire safety codes, county support for social services, and transit authority provision of special access vehicles for the aged and disabled.

Legislative policies are only a small piece of the public policy puzzle. Also important, for instance, are executive orders, court decisions, and decisions by regulatory agencies such as the Food and Drug Administration, the Federal Trade Commission, the Pension Benefit Guaranty Corporation, the Equal Employment Opportunity Commission, and many regulatory activities of states and localities such as health care licensing, oversight of private insurance sales practices, and zoning. State, county, and local referenda also affect older people, both as beneficiaries (e.g., of social services) and as taxpayers who fund services (e.g., through school bond levies).

Among the most important *private* sector policies related to aging and old age are the policies of employers toward workers and retirees. They include the provision and details of defined benefit pensions, defined contribution pensions, family leave policies for caregiving, and retiree health insurance. Although mandatory retirement has been outlawed in most sectors of American society since 1986 by the federal Age Discrimination in Employment Act, for several decades employers have been offering early retirement incentive programs (or buyouts) to reduce or "freshen" their workforces. Also among many policies deserving attention in the private sector are long-term care insurance and so-called Medigap insurance that provides coverage for health care expenses not covered by Medicare. As illustrated by the relationship between Medigap policies and the Medicare program, social policy education includes examination of the ways in which public and private sector policies complement and interact with each other.

The scope and emphasis of what one teaches about policy depends, of course, on the nature of the student body and/or the objectives of an overall curriculum or program as a whole. For instance, students in the applied professions—for example, physicians, nurses, rehabilitation professionals, clinical psychologists and social workers, hospital and long-term care administrators, financial advisors and counselors, lawyers, accountants, and the administrators and service providers in the Aging Services Network of the U.S. Administration on Aging—need to know, at the very least, the basic ABCs of the policies that directly affect their patients and clients. Practitioners in the health care arena, for example, can benefit their elderly patients by understanding the basics of Medicare, Medicaid, and Medigap eligibility and coverage, the differences between them, and the associated implications of referral, hospitalization, and discharge decisions. Consider that a 1-day stay in the hospital in 2008 would have cost $1,041 out-of-pocket (Centers for Medicare and Medicaid Services, 2008) for a low-income Medicare patient who was not poor enough to be eligible for Medicaid. Knowledge of this simple fact might have caused a geriatrician to think twice when she was making a borderline decision as to whether to hospitalize that patient. Similarly, social caseworkers need to be up-to-date on guardianship and elder-abuse laws in their states.

All students in gerontology and geriatrics should have familiarity with such policy fundamentals. But those who would be advocates, and policy analysts and researchers (including those researchers who also wear hats as practitioners), should be educated regarding a far broader range of more sophisticated historical, social, economic, and political contexts and issues involved with social policy and aging. Some of these contexts will be discussed later in this chapter.

RESOURCES FOR STUDENTS AND TEACHERS

In the age of the Internet, it is easy to identify and access resources that are helpful for teaching aging and social policy. In fact, the plethora of easily accessible electronic resources—added to social policy books, dozens of aging-related journals, more general policy journals, and policy analyses and reports from a variety of other sources—amplifies the educator's traditional challenge of selecting which materials to assign for reading and to use as bases for developing lectures and class discussions. Moreover, new developments in public and private sector policies related to aging are virtually continuous, requiring updates during the teaching of a course (or segment of a course) on aging and social policy. For instance, every spring the trustees of the Social Security and Medicare trust funds issue an annual report regarding the current status and projected condition of the funds for the years ahead. Frequently a vote is pending in Congress on a bill related to Medicare or other old-age policies. New Supreme Court decisions often affect the rights of older workers. The Pension Benefit Guaranty Corporation makes periodic reports to Congress on the status of defined benefit pension funds. Keeping up with such news in the policy world is demanding but essential.

Books and Journals

The selection of social policy readings for gerontology and geriatric students presents several challenges. First, as outlined earlier in this chapter, the scope of potential subject matter is extremely broad. As a consequence, no single textbook is likely to cover in reasonable depth a comprehensive range of policy subjects that a given instructor may desire. Second, new developments—whether policy changes, proposals for new and reformed policies, or broad trends (such as in the world of private-sector retiree benefits)—take place continuously. Therefore, social policy textbooks can become out-of-date rather quickly. Two recent paperback books that cover a relatively broad range of topics in social policy and aging, for instance, are *The New Politics of Old Age Policy* (Hudson, 2005) and *Aging Nation: The Economics and Politics of Growing Older in America* (Schulz & Binstock, 2008). (In the interest of full disclosure, I serve as consulting editor in gerontology for the publisher of these two books, Johns Hopkins University Press.) However, in these two volumes many of the policies that a particular instructor may wish to cover are only discussed in passing (e.g., the U.S. Administration on Aging and its Aging Services Network) or not mentioned at all (e.g., elder abuse policies). So instructors who choose to use these or other textbooks will often need to turn to additional sources for reading materials. For my own part, I have never used a textbook as the centerpiece of a course. Rather, I have constructed reading lists from a variety of sources, including selected chapters from books (e.g., Arza & Kohli, 2007; Binstock & George, 2006).

Journal articles, of course, can be excellent resources. As its title indicates, one such publication is the *Journal of Aging and Social Policy*. Lamentably, in recent years, social policy articles have rarely been published in the peer-reviewed journals of the Gerontological Society of America—*The Gerontologist* and the *Journals of Gerontology*—or in the *Journal of the American Geriatrics Society*. However, an Internet listing of about 60 *Journals on Aging* (Wood, 2007) includes some that do publish social policy articles from time to time. In addition, two periodicals that organize each issue around an aging-related theme—*Generations* and the *Public Policy and Aging Report*—often have articles that can be good choices for social policy and aging courses. Moreover, there are a number of other journals that publish excellent articles that are highly relevant to social policy and aging. Among them, for instance, are the *Social Security Bulletin, Health Affairs,* the *Milbank Quarterly,* the *Health Care Financing Review,* and the *American Journal of Public Health.*

Policy Research, Analyses, Issue Papers, and Breaking News

In addition, there is an abundance of useful policy research, analyses, and issue papers available from free-standing think tanks, institutes, and academies. Among them, for instance, are the Brookings Institution, the Cato Institute, the Employee Benefits Research Institute, the Heritage Foundation, the National Academies of Science (including, among others, the Institute of Medicine), the National Academy of Social Insurance, the National Bureau of Economic Research, the Rand Corporation's Center for the Study of Aging, and the Urban Institute.

Some of the old-age-based organizations that are among the 53 members of the Leadership Council of Aging Organizations are also sources of policy documents. These are produced, for instance, by entities such as AARP's Public Policy Institute, the Institute for the Future of Aging Services at the American Association of Homes and Services for the Aging, and the Gerontological Society's National Academy on an Aging Society. Others of these old-age–based organizations have not established specific policy entities but nonetheless produce informative policy documents. For example, the Older Women's League produces policy studies including an annual "Mother's Day Report." In addition to policy materials on its Web site, the National Council on Aging has a listserv that sends out up-to-date reports regarding day-to-day Congressional and other policy developments related to aging.

Foundations and university-based entities produce some excellent policy-related studies. Among foundations, the Commonwealth Fund and the

Kaiser Family Foundation frequently produce and fund many reports and studies that are relevant to health policy and aging. The Century Foundation issues occasional reports on social policy and aging.

Two of the most active university-based entities are the Center for Retirement Research at Boston College and its companion Michigan Retirement Research Center within the Institute for Social Research at the University of Michigan, which also houses the Health and Retirement Survey. Among many other centers at universities, for example, are the Center for Policy Research at Syracuse University and the Center on an Aging Society at Georgetown University.

Government agencies, of course, are a rich source of studies, surveys, and information relevant to social policy and aging. The Social Security Administration and the Centers for Medicare and Medicaid (CMS) are obvious starting points. In fact, a CMS booklet titled *Medicare and You,* distributed annually to Medicare enrollees (e.g., CMS, 2008), is an excellent resource for communicating to students the ABCs of Medicare. Other federal government agencies that are valuable sources include the Administration on Aging, the Bureau of Labor Statistics, the Census Bureau, the Centers for Disease Control and Prevention, the Congressional Budget Office, the Congressional Research Service, the Department of Veterans Affairs, the Employee Benefits Security Administration, the National Center for Health Statistics, the National Institute on Aging, the Office of Management and Budget, and the U.S. Government Accountability Office. Links to most of these, as well as other agencies, can be found on the Web site of the Federal Interagency Forum on Aging-Related Statistics, which also contains its own useful policy resources.

Finally, it is especially useful to be on listservs that provide frequent alerts to the availability of new documents and to media stories about new and emerging policy developments. The U.S. Government Accountability Office sends out almost daily a message titled "Today's GAO Reports," listing its new policy studies and written versions of testimony to Congress, with electronic links to each. The messages come from webmaster@gao.gov and are sent to daybook@listerv.gao.gov. The Commonwealth Foundation (commonwealthfund@cmwf.org) and the Kaiser Family Foundation (kaiser network@cme.kff.org) also issue frequent updates on health policy. Less frequent listserv messages, announcing new policy publications, are maintained by the Center for Retirement Research at Boston College (crr@bc.edu) and the Michigan Retirement Research Center (mrcc@isr.umich.edu). The Center for Demography of Health and Aging at the University of Wisconsin–Madison maintains two valuable listservs for policy teachers and researchers in the field of aging. One is a weekly *Current Awareness in Aging Report* that typically lists and provides links to dozens of reports and articles, many of which are policy relevant. The other is *Current Awareness in Aging E-Clippings*, which is sent out to the list every weekday. It provides links to media coverage of aging-related issues, mostly through newspapers (with an occasional record-ing), categorized by national stories and state and local stories. The men who provide these services are Jack Solock (jsolock@ssc.wisc.edu) and Charlie Fiss (fiss@ssc.wisc.edu). Of course, the E-Clippings service may not select the same policy stories that you would. So a useful practice is to check out di-rectly national newspapers such as the *New York Times*, the *Wall Street Journal*, and the *Washington Post*.

Visuals

Many technological advances in the use of visual materials have taken place during the decades I have been teaching social policy and aging. I've found them to have been extremely valuable in supplementing and enriching lec-tures and class discussions.

The development of PowerPoint has substantially enhanced an instruc-tor's opportunities to use visuals effectively. To be sure, for many decades it has been possible to create overheads and slides. But the processes of doing so are more cumbersome than creating PowerPoint presentations (which can easily be updated and revised). In addition, a set of PowerPoint slides can be made readily available to the computers of students, where they can be reviewed and studied outside of the classroom. Moreover, PowerPoint has made it pos-sible for colleagues to readily swap slides or entire presentations for teach-ing purposes, and for instructors to use ready-made presentations created by government agencies and other organizations. For instance, slides of all the charts in *Older Americans 2008: Key Indicators of Well-Being* can be downloaded from the Web site of the Federal Interagency Forum on Aging-Related Statis-tics (2008).

DVD and VHS videos (used sparingly) can bring to life key issue ar-eas that have been discussed in class, or set the stage for such discussions. In 2005, when President George W. Bush mounted a vigorous nationwide campaign to privatize Social Security, I videotaped a telecast speech by the then-president of AARP, Marie Smith. She laid out very effectively a number of reasons why her organization strongly opposed privatization, and made alternative proposals for Social Security reform.

Role-Playing

For advanced students, the experience of interactive role-playing in the policy world is an exceptionally good educational technique that can supplement or perhaps replace a traditional term paper. The instructor needs to create various situations involving a specific policy problem or issue, and cast a role both for the student as a presenter and for the instructor as an interactive responder (the latter, perhaps, joined by a student or two or by a faculty colleague).

For instance, a student can be assigned to provide written and oral testimony for a Congressional committee on policy issues and problems associated with the quality of care of older persons in nursing homes, with the instructor playing the role of the committee chair (and other students or colleagues joining in as committee members). Alternatively, a student might be asked to write a memo and meet with a U.S. president and/or top presidential advisors to provide a briefing on whether Social Security should be reformed, how, and the likely consequences. Or a student might play the role of a prospective buyer of long-term care insurance, writing out a series of questions to ask in a face-to-face meeting with an evasive long-term care insurance salesperson (the instructor). A student could even play the role of a nurse, physician, or social worker trying to provide written and one-on-one personal help to baffled patients (the instructor and others) who have confronted a series of specific issues and problems in the Medicare Part D prescription drug program. For all assignments, the students' written materials should be distributed to classmates ahead of time, and the interactive part of the assignment should take place in class. Fellow students can be asked to join the instructor in critiquing these presentations (both positively and remedially).

Although the steps necessary to set up these situations well requires a substantial investment of effort by the instructor, the payoffs are excellent. First, the role-playing students learn a great deal about the assigned topic. Second, they learn something about writing for various types of audiences in different formats and contexts. Third, their abilities to think on their feet are sharpened. And fourth, by entering a virtual setting where real world people may act on the basis of the student's analyses and responses to questions, the import of policy issues takes on more weight than what can be gleaned from readings, lectures, and class discussions.

CONCEPTS AND PERSPECTIVES IN TEACHING SOCIAL POLICIES

A great many concepts and perspectives are helpful in teaching social policy. For instance, in *Social Policy and Aging: A Critical Perspective,* Carroll Estes and her associates (Estes et al., 2001) present a number a political economy perspectives that elucidate effectively the many ways that the distribution of power in society affects social policies on aging and the status of older people.

In the remainder of this chapter, I will outline some of the selected concepts and perspectives that my students have found to be useful.

Heterogeneity, the Life-Course, and Social Structure

Two elementary principles are essential to convey in teaching social policy and in most other aspects of gerontology and geriatrics education. One, simply put, is: *older persons are heterogeneous.* The other is: *the full life-course and a great many socially structured impacts upon it (including the impacts of social policy) play a major role in shaping older people and their heterogeneity.*

When a particular birth cohort is young, it is highly diverse in personal characteristics. Some of these characteristics—such as gender, race, and ethnicity—remain unchanged throughout the life-course. Yet others can change markedly throughout a lifetime. For instance, differences in socioeconomic status, education, health, access to health care, and other inequalities within a cohort when it is young can be accentuated over time. Sociologist Dale Dannefer (2003) attributes this phenomenon to life-course processes he terms *cumulative advantage* and *cumulative disadvantage.* For those who are disadvantaged in youth, the opportunities for improvement are more limited than they are for the more advantaged. And over time the effects of such limitations and opportunities can be cumulative, widening the initial gaps.

The impact of social structure in exacerbating inequalities during the life-course is illuminated by considering the arena of retirement income where an individual's work history, public and private policies, and the market intersect. For example, a major factor in determining the size of checks for Social Security retirement benefits is the earnings history of the individual. Higher earners get higher benefits. Lower earners get lower benefits (although the benefits of low earners are proportionately more generous). Others, with limited education, who work in low-paying jobs that have no official payroll—such as many domestic workers and farm workers—have no earnings in the Social Security system to provide a basis for retirement benefits from the program. With this perspective it is clear why members of racial minorities in the United States—many of whom are employed in such jobs—are comparatively very poor in old age. While 7% of non-Hispanic Whites aged 65 and older have incomes that are below the official poverty line, the poverty rate for elderly Blacks and Hispanics are 23% and 19%, respectively (Federal Interagency Forum on Aging-Related Statistics, 2008, p. 12).

Similar situations prevail with respect to employer-sponsored pensions. Some employees work for firms that do not have pensions. For those who do work at a company that has a defined benefit pension plan, payments in retirement can be substantially different among individuals because the size of benefits may have been tailored to vary among different strata of employees. Or they may end up with sharply reduced benefits or none at all if their employer encounters major financial difficulties. And the pension benefits of those who work at a firm where defined contribution plans are available can vary substantially among individuals because the employer may tie different levels for its contributions to various categories of employees or levels of employee salaries. In addition, high earners can afford to make greater employee contributions to their plans than their lower-earning fellow workers.

In addition to retirement income, there are many other arenas in which social and economic differences within a cohort when it is young, combined with socially structured impacts during the life-course, account for heterogeneity of characteristics in old age. For instance, excellent health or disease and disability at younger ages—as well as differences in access to health care and new medical advances at various stages of the life-course—can have much to do with health and broader life circumstances at older ages.

These are but a few examples of life-course topics that can help students understand the many dimensions of heterogeneity among older people and identify interesting and important research questions to pursue. Many points can be made, of course, regarding how race, ethnicity, gender, economic and social status, and other characteristics play out differently through the life course into old age.

Policy Shapes Social Norms

Another basic principle is that social policy sets age norms throughout the life-course such as appropriate ages for attending school, driving, voting, making legal contracts, and so on. From its inception, Social Security's so-called normal retirement age (NRA) for full retired worker benefits obviously shaped and reinforced a cultural norm that 65 is a generally appropriate and expected age for retirement (even though the average age of retirement has been closer to 60 years of age for many decades). More broadly, the Social Security's NRA shaped the cultural labeling of *old people* and *the elderly* as persons aged 65 and older.

It was not until Bernice Neugarten (1974) demonstrated that people in their early 70s were much like those in their late 50s that the use of age 65 as a marker for *elderly* began to change, first among gerontologists and then, gradually, in American culture. By 1978, Congress outlawed mandatory retirement before the age of 70, and in 1986 it made mandatory retirement illegal at any age (except in certain public safety occupations, such as the police, firefighters, and airline pilots). These developments are now becoming gradually reinforced by changes in the NRA for Social Security benefits, presently over 66 years of age and moving toward the age of 67 in small increments. It would not be surprising if the NRA is raised further within the next few years, along with the age of eligibility for Medicare (now age 65), in response to federal budgetary pressures, particularly concerns about financing Social Security and Medicare as more and more baby boomers become eligible for those programs.

Models for Understanding the Politics of Public Policies

Why do specific public policies exist? And why do other potential policies that might be helpful to older persons or protect them from harm never seem to get on the policy agenda? Beyond the broad theoretical concepts for answering these questions, such as those in the volume by Estes and her associates (Estes et al., 2001), more proximate models for analyzing the politics of policymaking abound, and they are helpful tools for those who would aspire to be advocates on behalf of older persons. As the following examples of applying a few of many models will illustrate, such models are not mutually exclusive as explanations for a given policy.

Rational Solutions to Social Problems

Customary public discussions regarding public policies are implicitly based on the model that policies that have been enacted, or are being proposed, are solutions to social problems—furthering one or another (subjective) interpretation of the public interest. This construct provides a ready, straightforward explanation for the existence of Medicare.

When Medicare was initially enacted in 1965, the main source of health insurance in the United States (as is the case today) was employer-sponsored group health insurance. At the same time, mandatory retirement was common in most U.S. non-farm employment settings, customarily at the age of 65. Relatively few firms offered retiree health insurance, so most retired workers had to seek out health insurance as individuals in the marketplace. They had difficulty, however, in securing it. No longer part of a community-rated group, they could be excluded because of individual preexisting conditions determined through medical records and insurance company medical examinations. Even if they were not excluded, the premiums for coverage were expensive (and beyond the financial means of most retirees) because insurance companies were well aware that the rates of illness and disabilities rise exponentially among those aged in their late 60s and older. So the enactment of Medicare as a national health insurance program for virtually everyone aged

65 and older can be interpreted as a rational solution for the problem that a large group of Americans—that needed health insurance the most—was largely unable to get it.

This interpretation was reinforced by a 1972 amendment to Medicare that extended the program's coverage to persons receiving federal disability insurance. This group of individuals, by definition, is certified as not engaged in substantial work. Like most older persons, they are no longer part of an employer-sponsored group and find it very difficult to obtain health insurance. Again, a rational solution to a social problem.

Elite Preferences

In the mid-1950s, a book by sociologist C. Wright Mills (1956) opened the eyes of American society to the existence of what he called *The Power Elite*—consisting of celebrities, the "Big Rich," admirals and generals, top-level politicians, and corporation executives. "The power elite is composed of men whose positions enable them to transcend the ordinary environments of ordinary men and women; they are in positions to make decisions having major consequences" (pp. 3–4). Often, the establishment of new policies or the maintenance of existing polices can be interpreted as the preferences of such elites, in the private and public sectors, as they influence "the professional politicians of the middle levels of power, in the Congress and in the pressure groups" (p. 4). Elite power can also be used to keep certain issues from even reaching the policy agenda.

Explanations of policies that flow from this model are often difficult to document. Yet the passage of Medicare in 1965 presents an excellent example. Two of President Lyndon B. Johnson's top-level domestic policy advisers—Robert M. Ball (1995) and Wilbur J. Cohen (1985)—published personal accounts of their and the president's strategic thinking as they sought to have the program enacted. Basically, the president and his top domestic advisers hoped that if they could pass Medicare, that program would be the first in a series of incremental steps that would lead to national health insurance for all. The fact that the legislation solved the particular problems of access to health insurance only for retirees provided an excellent public interest rationale for the program that softened the potential opposition of interests groups (such as the American Medical Association) that strongly opposed national health insurance.

Interest Group Power

Another model tends to explain public policies as the outcome of conflicts and accommodations among special interest groups (pressure groups), with the most powerful groups getting their way. Why, for instance, did the Medicare Prescription Drug, Improvement, and Modernization Act (MMA) of 2003 contain a provision that explicitly prohibited the U.S. Secretary of Health and Human Services from directly negotiating for favorable drug prices with manufacturers, even though the Department of Veterans Affairs had already been doing this for its health care system? As many analysts of the politics of this legislation concluded, the prohibition in the MMA was due to the advocacy of the powerful pharmaceutical manufacturing industry, which contributes substantially to Congressional candidates through their political action committees (e.g., see Iglehart, 2004). (For a classic theoretical discussion of the role of interest groups in American politics, see Lowi [1979].)

Ideological Contexts of Social Policies
The ideological contexts in which old-age social policies emerge and change are important in teaching social policy because they provide broader and deeper understandings of existing policies. They also make clearer the political underpinnings of contemporary support for and opposition to those policies, as well as what's at stake in proposals to reform them.

The American Affinity for Classical Liberalism
Why did it take until 1935 for the United States to establish Social Security as a policy? Consider that Bismarck's proposed social insurance (or social security) scheme was established in Germany in 1889. During the next 25 years his approach was adopted in one form or another in many European countries—for example, Denmark in 1891, Belgium in 1894, France in 1903, Britain in 1908, and Sweden in 1913 (Schulz & Binstock, 2008). But it was only in the midst of the Great Depression of the 1930s that a U.S. Social Security retirement program was created by President Franklin Roosevelt, partly to reduce the number of older workers in the labor force so that younger unemployed workers would have less competition for jobs, as well as to provide income support in old age (Achenbaum, 1986). The long U.S. reluctance to adopt a Social Security program can be interpreted as reflecting a pervasive American liberal ideology that emphasized the primacy of individuals and the market and that avoided (as much as possible) welfare provided by the state.

Danish sociologist Gøsta Esping-Andersen, in sorting out different national approaches to issues of social risk, has distinguished between two ideal types. One type is *Homo liberalismus,* whose ideal is to pursue his personal welfare. "The well-being of others is their affair, not his. ... His ethics tell him that a free lunch is amoral, that collectivism jeopardizes freedom, that individual liberty is a fragile good, easily sabotaged by sinister socialists or paternalistic institutions. Homo liberalismus prefers a welfare regime where those who can play the market do so, whereas those who cannot must merit charity" (Esping-Andersen, 1999, p. 171). In contrast is *Homo socialdemocraticus* who "is fully convinced that the more we invest in the public good, the better it will become. And this will trickle down to all, himself especially, in the form of a good life. Collective solutions are the best single assurance of a good, if perhaps dull, individual life" (Esping-Andersen, 1999, pp. 171–172). Esping-Andersen argues that the United State and Sweden are the closest living embodiments of the dreams, respectively, of *Homo liberalismus* and *Homo socialdemocraticus.*

Most students of American political life would agree with Esping-Andersen's characterization of the predominant political ideology in the United States. Indeed, in his classic and influential treatise on *The Liberal Tradition in America,* political theorist Louis Hartz (1955) argued that our political ideas, institutions, and behavior have uniquely reflected a virtually unanimous acceptance of the tenets of the English political philosopher John Locke, whose ideas were in harmony with the laissez-faire economics subsequently propounded by Adam Smith (1776 [2003]). In Lockean liberalism, the individual is much more important than the collective, and one of the few important functions of a limited state is to ensure that the wealth that individuals accumulate through the market is protected (Locke, 1690 [1924]). In this ideological context, it is easier to understand why it took the economic and political crisis of the Great Depression to make possible the adoption of Social Security in the United States, long after it had become commonplace as a policy in most European nations.

Aging and the Rise of Collective Concern

The dire collective and individual effects of the Great Depression, especially the manifest failures of the free market, made possible the acceptance (though not universal) of Franklin Roosevelt's New Deal programs to deal with market failures. The classical liberal ideology that characterized the American polity was temporarily submerged while a norm of activist government evolved from the New Deal, through World War II, and beyond. Both Republican and Democratic presidents maintained this norm through five decades.

The ideological bulwark of individual responsibility was especially broken with Social Security's establishment in 1935—a policy that singled out older Americans as a special group that needed to be collectively insured against the risks associated with old age. This new norm regarding older people, embodied in Social Security, was amplified in the years that followed. From the mid-1930s through the late 1970s the construction of an old-age welfare state was facilitated by a compassionate ageism—the attribution of the same characteristics, status, and just deserts to a heterogeneous group of the aged that tended to be stereotyped as poor, frail, dependent, objects of discrimination, and above all "deserving" (Kalish, 1979).

The stereotypes expressed through this ageism, unlike those of racism or sexism, were not wholly prejudicial to the well-being of its objects, older people. During five decades the American polity implemented the construct of compassionate ageism by creating many old-age government benefit programs, as well as by enacting laws against age discrimination. During the 1960s and 1970s, just about every issue or problem affecting some older persons that could be identified by advocates for the elderly became a governmental responsibility. Programs were enacted to provide older Americans with: health insurance (Medicare and Medicaid); nutritional, legal, supportive, and leisure services (Older Americans Act); housing; home repair; energy assistance; transportation; help in getting jobs; protection against being fired from jobs; public insurance for employer-sponsored pensions; special mental health programs; and on and on. By the late 1970s, if not earlier, American society had learned the catechism of compassionate ageism very well and had expressed it through a great many policies.

Aging and the Resurgence of Classical Liberalism
Then, after decades in which Social Security and the other old-age policies had become politically accepted as staples, the ideological pendulum swung away from collective concerns. Classical liberal ideology reemerged and flourished. This neoliberalism (popularly labeled as *conservatism*) once again emphasized the virtues of atomistic individualism and the virtues of free-market capitalism, while also stressing the evils of so-called big government, including government regulation and welfare programs (see Pierson & Skocpol, 2007) This ideological context is important for understanding public political discourse and proposals for changing old-age policies today.

Neoliberalism emerged at the end of the 1970s and has persisted into the 21st century, spearheaded by the actions of a series of U.S. presidents. In the early 1980s, for instance, Ronald Reagan froze an annual cost-of-living adjustment in Social Security benefits, proposed (unsuccessfully) to make drastic cuts in the program's benefits, greatly tightened eligibility determination for federal disability insurance under Social Security, and deregulated a number of industries. In the 1990s, Bill Clinton vowed to "end welfare as we know it" and "end big government," and he made progress on both fronts. The title of the welfare reform bill that Clinton signed into law expressed neoliberalism in clear terms. It was called The Personal Responsibility and Work Opportunity Reconciliation Act of 1996.

When George W. Bush took office in 2001, he had a long history of ideological distaste for the Social Security program and all government interventions. According to one of his professors at Harvard Business School in the mid-1970s, in his class Bush denounced Franklin Roosevelt as a socialist, and specifically identified Social Security as one of several Roosevelt New Deal programs that he wanted to undo (Tsurumi, 2006). Bush spent the 8 years of his presidency promoting what he called "The Ownership Society," in which market forces (rather than government) are looked to for solutions to problems and individuals take on more responsibility for their welfare. He successfully led the passage of the MMA in 2003, which converted substantial portions of Medicare to private-sector markets. In 2005, Bush traveled throughout the country proclaiming that Social Security was in a *crisis,* and tried very hard (though unsuccessfully) to convert much of the Social Security program into individual privatized accounts.

At the same time that classical liberalism was reemerging, the compassionate stereotypes that had facilitated the building of an old-age welfare state underwent an extraordinary reversal. Older Americans began to be depicted by pernicious negative stereotypes and, as a group, became a scapegoat for a variety of societal problems. A key precipitating factor in the development of older people as a scapegoat was that in the late 1970s journalists (e.g., Samuelson, 1978) and academicians (e.g., Hudson, 1978) discovered "the graying of the budget," a tremendous growth in federal funds spent on old-age benefits that had made them comparable in size to spending for national defense. By 1982 an economist in the Office of Management and Budget had pointed up the comparison with the defense budget by reframing the classical trade-off metaphor of political economy from "guns vs. butter" to "guns vs. canes" (Torrey, 1982).

Whereas elderly persons had previously been stereotyped as poor and deserving, they now began to be portrayed as flourishing and a burden to society. As *Forbes* magazine succinctly and patronizingly expressed the new wisdom concerning "old folks": "The myth is that they're sunk in poverty. The reality is that they're living well. The trouble is there are too many of them—God bless 'em" (Flint, 1980, p. 51).

Throughout the 1980s and well into the 1990s, the new stereotypes, readily observed in popular culture, presented older people as prosperous, hedonistic, politically powerful, and selfish. A dominant theme in such accounts of older people was that their selfishness was ruining the nation. The epithet "greedy geezers" became a familiar adjective in journalistic accounts of federal budget politics (e.g., Salholz, 1990). And *Fortune* magazine went so far as to declaim that the "tyranny of America's old" was "one of the most crucial issues facing U.S. society" (Smith, 1992, p. 68).

Meanwhile, the looming eligibility of aging baby boomers for old-age benefits (and projected aggregate costs of those benefits) brought programs for the aging under attack, especially Social Security and Medicare. A variety of politicians, policy pundits, academicians, and journalists began to publicly characterize the aging of boomers as a *crisis* portending financial catastrophe for our nation, and they continue to do so through today (see Schulz & Binstock, 2008). Not surprisingly given the context of neoliberalism, many of these doomsayers promote reforms such as privatization of Social Security that would reduce the role of government and promote the free market. Such a reform would rely on the individual and market forces, rather than government, to provide income benefits in old age. Moreover, at present, Social Security annually redirects more than half a trillion dollars from the private sector to the public sector. Privatization would recapture most of that for the private sector.

A Perspective on Crises
Education that brings out concepts and perspectives such as those previously discussed provides students of gerontology and geriatrics—especially those who would be advocates—with important contexts for understanding and dealing with the world of social policy and aging. At present, for instance, that world is permeated with portrayals of crises in the old-age welfare state, which serve as springboards for radical reform proposals. To be sure, the rapid aging of our population between now and 2030 presents substantial policy challenges. Yet some historical perspective on declamations of so-called crises in the old-age policy arena reveals that they have been off the mark. Consider the following examples.

When Medicare was proposed (and finally enacted in 1965), leaders of the American Medical Association—a vigorous opponent of the legislation—made the ominous prediction that the program would quickly lead to "socialized medicine," causing a crisis in health care. No such thing happened. In the late 1970s and early 1980s, there was a so-called crisis in Social Security financing. Despite the extensive crisis rhetoric at the time, it turned out that the financing problem was not terribly difficult to solve. Still another crisis was perceived in 1986 when Congress outlawed mandatory retirement at any age for almost all jobs. Many employers foresaw economic disaster. They predicted that business payrolls would be overwhelmed and production clogged by large numbers of very old, highly paid workers whose skills and energy had diminished with age. Once again, the fears turned out to be unfounded. Relatively few older persons chose to work longer (and most that did were highly productive). Historical perspectives such as these provide students with valuable contexts for thinking about present-day policy issues and debates.

Present shouts of "crisis" are not much different from the past, except perhaps for the massive uncertainty they are generating about the fate of Social Security and Medicare. By putting aside the rhetoric of crisis, it is relatively easy to see that the challenges of sustaining Social Security can be met through minor changes that do not require radical reform. It can also be easy to look at, and learn from, the experiences of many relatively recent reforms of old-age policies that have taken place in other industrialized nations of the world. Many of those countries have proportions of older persons that the United States will not achieve for several decades. Yet they have been able to achieve reforms in pensions, long-term care, and other areas of policy on aging without crises and intergenerational conflict (e.g., see Arza & Kohli, 2007).

Future U.S. elderly generations face an increasing number of years in old age, and exactly what that life will be like is unclear. But the current crisis proposals, if not placed into broader perspectives, could very well lead, at the extreme, to the destruction of the spectacular past gains in old-age security that were brought about through social policies on aging in the 20th century. Students in gerontology and geriatrics who aim to be advocates should be especially alerted to this possibility.

REFERENCES

Achenbaum, W. A. (1986). *Social Security: Visions and revisions*. New York: Cambridge University Press.

Arza, C., & Kohli, M. (Eds.). (2007). *Pension reform in Europe: Politics, policies and outcomes*. London: Routledge

Ball, R. M. (1995). What Medicare's architects had in mind. *Health Affairs, 14*(4), 62–72.

Binstock, R. H., & George, L. K. (Eds.). (2006). *Handbook of aging and the social sciences* (6th ed.). San Diego, CA: Academic Press.

Centers for Medicare and Medicaid Services. (2008). *Medicare and you: 2008*. Baltimore, MD: U.S. Department of Health and Human Services.

Cohen, W. J. (1985). Reflections on the enactment of Medicare and Medicaid. *Health Care Financing Review*, Annual Supplement, 3–11.

Dannefer, D. (2003). Cumulative advantage/disadvantage and the life course: Cross-fertilizing age and social science theory. *The Journals of Gerontology Series B: Psychological Sciences and Social Sciences, 58,* S327–S337.

Esping-Andersen, G. (1999). *Social foundations of postindustrial economies.* New York: Oxford University Press.

Estes, C. L., Alford, R. R., Binney, E. A., Bradsher, J. E., Close, L., Collins, C. A., et al., (2001). *Social policy and aging: A critical perspective.* Thousand Oaks, CA: Sage Publications.

Federal Interagency Forum on Aging-Related Statistics. (2008). *Older Americans 2008: Key indicators of well-being.* Retrieved June 16, 2008, from http://aging stats.gov/agingstatsdotnet/main_site/default.aspx

Flint, J. (1980, February 18). The old folks. *Forbes,* 51–56.

Hartz, L. (1995). *The liberal tradition in America.* New York: Harcourt Brace and Company.

Hudson, R. B. (1978). The "graying" of the federal budget and its consequences for old age policy. *Gerontologist, 18,* 428–440.

Hudson, R. B. (Ed.). (2005). *The new politics of old age.* Baltimore, MD: Johns Hopkins University Press.

Iglehart, J. K. (2004). The new Medicare prescription-drug benefit—a pure power play. *New England Journal of Medicine, 350,* 826–833.

Kalish, R. A. (1979). The new ageism and the failure models: A polemic. *Gerontologist, 19,* 398–407.

Locke, J. (1690 [1924]). *Of civil government, two treatises.* London: J. M. Dent & Sons,.

Lowi, T. H. (1979). *The end of liberalism: The second republic of the United States.* New York: W. W. Norton & Company.

Mills, C. W. (1956). *The power elite.* New York: Oxford University Press.

Neugarten, B. L. (1974). Age groups in American society and the rise of the young-old. *Annals of the American Academy of Political and Social Science, 415,* 187–198.

Pierson, P., & Skocpol, T. (Eds.). (2007). *The transformation of American politics: Activist government and the rise of conservatism.* Princeton, NJ: Princeton University Press.

Salholz, E. (1990, October 29). Blaming the voters: Hapless budgeteers single out "greedy geezers." *Newsweek,* 36.

Samuelson, R. J. (1978). Aging America: Who will shoulder the growing burden? *National Journal, 10,* 712–1717.

Schulz, J. H., & Binstock, R. H. (2008). *Aging nation: The economics and politics of growing older in America.* Baltimore, MD: The Johns Hopkins University Press.

Smith, A. (1776 [2003]). *The wealth of nations.* New York: Bantam Classics.

Smith, L. (1992). The tyranny of America's old. *Fortune, 125*(1), 68–72.

Torrey, B. B. (1982). Guns vs. canes: The fiscal implications of an aging population. *American Economics Association Papers and Proceedings, 72,* 309–313.

Tsurumi, Y. (2006, April 6). Hail to the robber baron? *The Harvard Crimson.* Retrieved April 8, 2005, from http:///www.thecrimson.com/printerfriendly.aspx?ref=506836

Wood, M. D. (2007). *Journals on aging* (updated December 20). Retrieved June 11, 2008, from http://crab.rutgers.edu/~deppen/journals.htm

CHAPTER 7

Cultural Diversity in Geriatrics and Gerontology Education

Gwen Yeo and Melen McBride

The educational experiences available in cultural diversity and aging are almost as diverse as the elders themselves. Faculty in many disciplines have found many different ways to try to prepare students to meet the challenges of an increasingly heterogeneous population of older adults. The realizations that elders from populations defined officially as minorities will probably be one-third of older Americans by the middle of the 21st century (Federal Interagency Forum on Aging Related Statistics, 2000), that there is vast diversity within each of these populations and within the White majority, and that there are unique cultural needs and issues associated with each group have prompted increasing attention to cultural diversity in gerontology and geriatrics instruction during the last four decades.

HISTORICAL BACKGROUND OF CULTURAL DIVERSITY EDUCATION IN GERIATRICS AND GERONTOLOGY

The evolution of curricula and models of instruction in the fields that have come to be known as ethnogerontology and ethnogeriatrics are even more recent than that of their relatively new parent disciplines of gerontology and geriatrics themselves. Not until the late 1980s and early 1990s were there descriptions of specific educational programs focusing on cultural diversity of older adults.

DOI: 10.1891/0198-8794.28.93

One of the fields from which ethnogerontology and ethnogeriatrics emerged was anthropology, with its descriptions of distinct cultures. These descriptions frequently included the cultures' definitions of age stratification and roles of distinct ages and generations. Examples of the anthropological perspective that informed early ethnogerontology are the book edited by Gelfand and Kutzik in 1979, *Ethnicity and Aging: Theory, Research, and Practice,* and the founding of the Association of Anthropology and Gerontology (AAGE) in 1978.

Other early influences were the writings of Jacqueline J. Jackson, from Duke University, who is generally credited with bringing attention to the field and developing the term ethnogerontology, emphasizing the influence of race, national origin, and culture on the aging of both the individual and populations (Jackson, 1976). At about the same time, James S. Jackson at the University of Michigan was building a research center focusing on Black aging, recruiting faculty with that expertise, and publishing excellent sources of information for faculty to use in their ethnogerontology courses. Percil Stanford and other members of the San Diego State University Center on Minority Aging, funded by the Administration on Aging (AoA), conducted research among elders from Black, American Indian, Chinese, Guamanian, Japanese, Latino, Filipino, and Samoan ethnic backgrounds in San Diego during the mid 1970s; the results were published in individual monographs describing their demographic characteristics and health needs (Valle, 1976) which were used as the basis for teaching by many faculty. AoA also began funding advocacy organizations for elders from four ethnic minority populations in 1973; these organizations (National Caucus and Center on Black Aging, National Hispanic Council on Aging, National Indian Council on Aging, and National Asian Pacific Center on Aging) also helped to bring emphasis to the needs of their target populations and developed information used for curriculum.

With the realization in the 1980s of the growing diversity of the U.S. population, including older adults, gerontologists began to recognize the need to prepare students to work with the culturally heterogeneous populations of elders. In 1988 we reviewed the listings in the 1987 *National Directory of Educational Programs* published by the Association of Gerontology in Higher Education (AGHE) (Peterson, Bergstone, & Lobenstine, 1987) for content in "ethnic" or "minority" or "cross-cultural" issues in aging. Of the 404 colleges and universities with listings in the AGHE directory, 41 had a reference to ethnogerontological content, 16 of which were in health care disciplines. The most common pattern seemed to be a class in ethnicity and aging in anthropology or ethnic studies programs for students in different fields (Yeo, 1988).

Growing out of concerns of key staff about lack of curriculum in minority aging, the Bureau of Health Professions (BHPr) of the Health Resources and Services Administration (HRSA) and other governmental agencies sponsored a national invitational 2-day conference for experts on health care for minority elders and geriatric educators in 1988 to focus on development of curriculum content and approaches in teaching health professionals issues that affect the health care of elders from disadvantaged minority backgrounds. One of the outcomes was a widely used book edited by Dr. Mary Harper, *Minority Aging: Essential Curricula Content for Selected Health and Allied Health Professions* (1990), which included 42 chapters reviewing the major demographic, health status, utilization, and treatment literature for each of the four disadvantaged minority populations along with curriculum recommendations.

In 1988 members of Stanford Geriatric Education Center's (SGEC) multidisciplinary, multiethnic Affiliated Core Faculty focused their work on the field they named "ethnogeriatrics" and as one of their first efforts reviewed 41 geriatrics textbooks for ethnogeriatric content, defined as material combining the three basic components of health, aging, and ethnicity. Seventeen (41%) had some reference to ethnogeriatric issues. These included 100% of the 3 psychology, 71% of the 7 social work, 47% of the 15 gerontological nursing, and 13% of the 15 geriatric medicine text books; the one geriatric occupational therapy textbook had no ethnic content (Yeo, 1990). A list of recommended ethnogeriatric competencies was also developed as part of a framework to develop curricula and teaching resources (Yeo, 1989).

Ethnogeriatric education received a major impetus for growth with the funding preferences given by BHPr for applicants for Geriatric Education Centers (GECs). Beginning in 1987, and gradually expanding through the 1990s, preferences were given to applicants who proposed curriculum development in minority aging and/or training educators or practitioners who serve minority or low-income elderly (Klein, 1996b). By 1990 ethnogeriatric education was blossoming, especially in the GECs. A 1990 symposium at the American Society on Aging (ASA) meetings documented 24 modules or other teaching units developed by 12 GECs, 13 monographs, 7 videotapes, and 36 conferences featuring ethnogeriatric topics sponsored by 20 GECs; 13 centers had clinical ethnogeriatric training sites, and 3 had computerized ethnogeriatric bibliographic data bases (Yeo, 1992).

Other major developments in the early 1990s included:

- *Teaching About Aging: Interdisciplinary and Cross-Cultural Perspectives,* a book compiled and disseminated by the Association for Anthropology and Gerontology, contained 30 course outlines from various universities, most of which were taught in anthropology programs (Francis, Shenk, & Sokolovsky, 1990).

- "Ethnic Diversity: Barrier or Benefit in Health Care for the Elderly," a 1991 teleconference sponsored by Virginia Commonwealth GEC attended by several thousand participants, included a discussion of educational as well as clinical and policy topics.
- The Gerontological Society on Aging (GSA) came out with the first in an ongoing series of publications on minority aging topics that are widely used for teaching resources and is still being published from time to time.
- Stanford and Meharry GECs, San Jose State University, and the Palo Alto Veterans Administration Geriatric Research, Education, and Clinical Center (GRECC) sponsored a 2-day conference in 1992 titled "Ethnogeriatric Curriculum: What Should We Teach and How Should We Teach It?" which was attended by 94 faculty from 11 disciplines and 16 states.
- The U.S. House Select Committee on Aging developed a chapter outlining the needs and recommendations for ethnogeriatric training in a publication on the shortage of trained health care professionals serving older adults (Yeo, 1993).
- There was increasing emphasis on minority aging issues in all of the national aging organizations, including AGHE, American Geriatrics Society (AGS), ASA, and GSA, most of whom have special task forces or committees on minority aging that help to provide educational programs for annual meetings and develop educational resources.
- Specific ethnogerontology or ethnogeriatric curricula was published in textbooks or curriculum guides in individual disciplines, including medicine, nursing, occupational therapy, optometry, psychology, public health, and social work (Klein, 1996b).
- An ethnogeriatrics mini-fellowship, a 120-hour independent study and customized program for faculty, clinicians, and graduate students at the Stanford GEC was developed and continues to the present.

In 1995, BHPr sponsored a forum titled "A National Agenda for Geriatric Education," which was attended by leading educators in the field of aging from multiple health care disciplines. In preparation for the forum, BHPr commissioned the development of 11 White Papers on the state of the art and recommendations for education in geriatrics for six disciplines and five cross-cutting issues, one of which was ethnogeriatrics. The report of the forum and the White Papers were published in 1996 (Klein, 1996a, 1996b) and were influential in directing the course of funding and curriculum development in ethnogeriatrics and the other components of geriatric education through the turn of the century.

CURRENT CURRICULUM AND INSTRUCTION IN ETHNOGERONTOLOGY AND ETHNOGERIATRICS

Curriculum in Ethnogeriatrics

Building on the recommendations from the ethnogeriatrics White Paper, BHPr formed a task force on ethnogeriatrics charged with identifying training needs in the area. The task force recommended that a curriculum in ethnogeriatrics in two parts be developed that would be appropriate for all health care disciplines. The core curriculum would contain basic content for cultural competence in health care for older adults. They also recommended that ethnic-specific modules be developed so that faculty could choose focused information on the populations of interest in their areas to be taught in conjunction with the basic core curriculum. The ethnic-specific modules would emphasize the heterogeneity within the ethnic populations to try to decrease the learners' tendency to use the information to develop or reinforce stereotypes.

With funding from BHPr, The Collaborative on Ethnogeriatric Education with representatives from 34 GECs in different parts of the United States was formed and coordinated by Stanford GEC to develop the recommended curriculum in ethnogeriatrics and associated resources for faculty. The five modules in the core curriculum were written by 21 authors from 14 different GECs. The modules are: 1. Introduction and Overview, 2. Patterns of Health Risk, 3. Culturally Appropriate Geriatric Care: Fund of Knowledge, 4. Culturally Appropriate Geriatric Care: Assessment, and 5. Culturally Appropriate Geriatric Care: Health Care Interventions, Access, and Utilization. Each includes a description, learning objectives, content outline, instructional strategies and resources, an evaluation plan, and references and resources. Appendices include: explanations of significant concepts in ethnogeriatrics, a link to the census form used in the 2000 census, and instructional strategies for interviewing elders from diverse ethnic backgrounds.

The 12 ethnic-specific modules follow the same outlines as the core curriculum modules and were written by 29 authors, most from the target populations, in 8 different GECs. The topics are health and health care for each of the following populations: African American elders, American Indian/Alaska Native elders, Hispanic/Latino elders (including Mexican American, Puerto Rican, and Cuban American), and Asian and Pacific Islander (API) elders. This is followed by modules on elders from the following specific API populations: Asian Indian American, Chinese American, Filipino American, Japanese American, Korean American, Native Hawaiian and other Pacific Islander, Pakistani American, and Southeast Asian American (including Vietnamese, Cambodian,

Hmong, and Laotian). Each of the modules includes descriptions, learning objectives, a narrative description of the content, instructional strategies, specific test questions to evaluate learner's understanding, cases for discussion, and references and resources.

A Web site (http://www.stanford.edu/group/ethnoger) was developed in 2001 for both sections of the curriculum in ethnogeriatrics for general access at no cost. When the Web site was established, a request for visitors to the Web site to complete a short questionnaire was included and later made more prominent to try to increase response. However, the survey is completed by only a small fraction of the number of individuals who visit the Web site. Based on the survey responses as of February 2008, information from GECs, and faculty who have contacted Stanford GEC, some or all of the curriculum in ethnogeriatrics has been or is being used by faculty in programs in 214 colleges and universities in 41 states and 5 foreign countries from 17 different disciplines. In addition, the curriculum is being used by training programs in hospitals, rehabilitation facilities, Area Agencies in Aging, Area Health Education Centers, nursing homes, hospices, secondary school districts, community service agencies, and home health agencies.

With funding from BHPr, specifically through the Comprehensive Geriatric Education Program (CGEP), the modules of the curriculum in ethnogeriatrics are being updated, and multimedia resources are being developed to make them easier for faculty to use. An addition to the updated resource are modules on Hmong American elders and on Native Alaska elders and an educator's guide to incorporate ethnogeriatrics in nursing education programs (McBride, 2008).

Survey of Member Institutions of the Association of Gerontology in Higher Education (AGHE)

Another indication of the growth in ethnogeriatric and ethnogerontological education came through AGHE. In January 2008, an electronic survey was sent by AGHE to over 750 colleges and universities to determine whether cultural diversity content was included in their programs (see Table 7.1). All but two of the 142 responders indicated that cultural diversity content was part of the curriculum. Respondents were from 39 states and Canada, with the most responses coming from California (12%) followed by Maryland (7%), Massachusetts, Missouri, New York, and North Carolina (6% each). There were two or more responders from the same institution in 10 cases, although the programs were from different departments. A variety of gerontology and geriatric courses were offered at the participating public and private universities and colleges, and Veterans Administration Health Care Systems. Forty-one percent offered cultural diversity courses, and 98% incorporated the content in various courses (see Table 7.1). Lectures, case discussions, interactive exercises, and reading assignments were the most popular approaches to delivering cultural diversity content. Other strategies used are different types of media, online, and Internet technology (34%), including WebCT. Other innovative methods include family history through genograms, independent or group projects, service learning or clinical internship assignments, a teaching panel of elders of color, local field trips for performances or community education/outreach events, and short-term international cultural immersion. Eighteen percent of the programs offer independent studies or research projects focused on cultural diversity or ethnogeriatrics. Eight institutions have postgraduate fellowships in gerontology, geriatrics, or ethnogeriatrics. Specialization in gerontology/geriatrics are offered in undergraduate (47%), master's (44%), doctoral (22%), certificate (63%), and continuing education (17%) programs, and minors for different program levels (11%). One institution offers an online gerontology certificate program, and others specifically offered graduate level certificate programs (10%) for various disciplines.

There are institutions with multiple gerontology/geriatrics programs from different departments or divisions such as business administration, education, gerontology, health/human sciences, liberal arts, medicine, nursing, nutritional science, pharmacy, political science, public health, psychology, recreation/sports sciences, social work, sociology, and centers/institutes on aging. This wide range of institutional support has many opportunities to offer course-specific or integrated content on cultural diversity or ethnogeriatrics. One institution indicated a cultural diversity course included lesbian, gay, bisexual, and transgender (LGBT) content. Some responders indicated the precarious nature of gerontology programs in their setting, such as: discontinuance,

TABLE 7.1
Respondents to AGHE Survey

	Number	Percent
With cultural diversity content	140	99
Courses in cultural diversity	58	41
Cultural diversity incorporated into other course content	139	98
Independent study or research projects in cultural diversity	26	18
Use of media, online, or Internet for cultural diversity instruction	48	34

Note. N = 142 programs or institutions.

merging with other specialties, reestablishment of previous aging programs, competing priorities from cross-specialization of faculty, and limited resources for faculty release time and student recruitment.

Curricular Framework and Core Competencies in Multicultural Geriatric Care

In an effort to assist educators in developing programs to meet the needs for training in cultural competence for geriatric providers, a working group composed of representatives from the Ethnogeriatrics Committee of AGS and the University of California Academic Geriatric Resource Centers developed a curricular framework for multicultural geriatric care consisting of a comprehensive set of competencies and recommended instructional strategies (Cultural Competencies Writing Group, 2004). The core competencies focused on attitudes, knowledge, and skills especially appropriate for medical education. The framework and core competencies were published in the *Journal of American Geriatrics Society* in 2004 and included resources for faculty.

MAJOR RESOURCES FOR ETHNOGERONTOLOGY AND ETHNOGERIATRICS EDUCATION

One indication of the strength of educational programs in cultural diversity and aging is the plethora of current resources available for faculty. In addition to the curriculum in ethnogeriatrics and other resources described previously in this chapter, major sets of materials for teachers in cultural diversity and aging are described in the following section.

Association for Gerontology in Higher Education (AGHE) Bibliographies

The AGHE has developed and published, and updated in 2004, a series of "AGHE Brief Bibliographies on Diversity Topics in aging" for faculty to use in developing courses in cultural diversity. (They can be ordered from AGHE at http://www.aghe.org/site/aghewebsite/content.php?type=1&id=8076.) These include the following:

- *American Indian Aging.* Compiled by Robert John (2004).
- *Asian American and Pacific Islander Elders.* Compiled by Barbara Yee and Gwen Yeo (2004).
- *Cultural Perspectives on Aging.* Compiled by Dena Shenk and Jay Sokolovsky (2004).

- *Ethnogerontology and African Americans.* Compiled by Keith E. Whitfield and Martha R. Crowther (2004).
- *Hispanic/Latino Gerontology.* Compiled by Steven Applewhite and Cruz C. Torres (2004).
- *International Aging.* Compiled by Charlotte Nusberg and Jay Sokolovsky (2004).

Resources From Geriatric Education Centers
National Clearinghouse for Geriatric Education Resources
The BHPr of the HRSA funded the creation of a catalogue of geriatrics/gerontology educational resources developed by HRSA-funded Geriatric Education Centers. The purpose of the clearinghouse is to:

- Provide health professional faculty, practitioners, and students with information on aging and geriatrics education resources available through the GECs,
- Encourage collaboration among geriatrics education providers,
- Reduce redundant efforts in geriatrics education programming, and
- Facilitate the identification of areas where further development of geriatrics education materials is needed.

The types of resources listed consist of curricula, audiovisual materials, education technology resources, (e.g., online modules, webcasts), monographs, case studies and discussion guides, and conference programs. The clearinghouse is currently maintained by the Kansas GEC and can be accessed at http://coa. kumc.edu/gecresource.

An electronic search of resources with cultural diversity or ethnogeriatric content was made using the following terms: cultural diversity, ethnogeriatrics, cultural competency, minority elders, racial/ethnic elders, ethnic-specific designations, health literacy, and health disparity. A total of 63 entries were found under these terms developed by 18 GECs (36% of HRSA-funded GECs). For ethnogeriatrics, 31 resources were found from 8 GECs; minority elders and cultural competency titles had 19 and 9, respectively; 17 ethnic-specific resources were found. Duplicate listings for these categories were noted, such as African American elders, and topics on caregiving and elder abuse. These include curricula, conference reports, videos, and online resources.

Ethnogeriatric Curriculum
In addition to the curriculum in ethnogeriatrics developed by the inter-GEC collaborative on ethnogeriatrics education mentioned previously, South Carolina

GEC has produced a comprehensive peer-reviewed ethnogeriatric curriculum. It consists of four modules: (a) adaptive communication activities with minority elderly consumers; (b) African American elderly consumer: cultural myths and health-seeking behaviors; (c) ethnogeriatric health disparities and the minority elderly; and (d) ethnogeriatric strategies in delivering health care to minority elders.

Mental Health Resources

In 2004, the faculty at Stanford GEC developed an ethnogeriatric curriculum titled "Mental Health Aspects of Diabetes in Elders from Diverse Backgrounds" (Yeo, 2004). It includes an overview module, seven ethnic-specific modules (African American, American Indian, Chinese American, Filipino American, Hmong American, Japanese American, and Mexican American), and a section on emergency preparedness for ethnic elders with diabetes-related sensory changes. In each of the ethnic-specific sections, the risks of diabetes, dementia, and depression are reviewed along with culturally appropriate assessment and management for each of the three conditions for elders from that particular ethnic population. Particularly important resources are sections on nutrition issues and recommendations for older adults with diabetes in each ethnic population, and common complementary and alternative therapies used for diabetes in each population.

In 2005 the Consortium of New York GECs implemented a 5-day curriculum for a certificate program titled "Geriatric Mental Health and Disaster Preparedness" with ethnogeriatric content infused into five modules: day 1: introduction to geriatric emergency preparedness; day 2: problem-solving in a team context; day 3: systems and networks; day 5: mental health and quality of life; and day 5: self-care and integrative modalities. The fifth module included content on spirituality and healing from different cultural perspectives and ways to ease a recovery process (McBride, 2006).

A community–academic partnership between the Asian Pacific Fund, Stanford GEC and AARP enabled them to produce a 20-minute health education video titled *Healing the Spirit: Treatment of Depression Among the Asian Elderly* (Asian Pacific Fund, AARP, & Stanford GEC, 2003). The goal of the video was to educate clinicians and the community about the high suicide rate among Asian older women and to motivate the Asian community to seek professional help. Each DVD or videotape contains the film in nine languages: Cantonese, English, Hindi, Japanese, Khmer, Korean, Mandarin, Tagalog and Vietnamese. Analysis of historical events and access barriers are ethnogeriatric concepts presented through the experiences of three older Asian American women who were under treatment for depression. The resource has been widely distributed to nonprofit service groups providing primary care and social services to Asian communities, academic programs, public libraries, and health professional organizations. The film has been well received at professional meetings of physicians, gerontologists, health care providers, and students in health and aging. A user's guide and an evaluation form accompany the video. Additional information on this ethnogeriatric resource is available at http://www.asianpacificfund.org/resource/healthvideo.shtml

Cultural Diversity Online Information Source

An online ethnogeriatric resource titled "Diversity, Healing, and Health Care" was developed by Bonnie Napier-Tibere, PhD, OTR, in collaboration with the Stanford GEC and OnLok Senior Health Services for a doctoral dissertation project in educational technology. The Web-based resource intended for clinicians "on-the-run" has content on practical and culturally appropriate approaches for interacting with older adults from different ethnic groups. The material is presented in three modules: greetings and introductions for 15 ethnic groups, religious beliefs and healing for 12 different religions, and cohort life events for 8 ethnic groups. Content is brief and quick to read as "just-in-time" and "on-demand" information that can be applied immediately as needed by the clinician. A bibliographic list provides the user with research-based publications. It is available at http://www.gasi-ves.org/diversity.htm (McBride & Napier-Tibere, 2004).

American Geriatrics Society Initiatives

In addition to educational programs on ethnogeriatrics during the AGS annual meetings, education of clinicians was the goal for several initiatives of the Ethnogeriatric Committee of the American Geriatrics Society. They include establishment of an ethnogeriatrics section of the *Journal of the American Geriatrics Society (JAGS)* and the publication of a three-volume series titled *Doorway Thoughts: Cross-Cultural Health Care for Older Adults* (Adler, 2006; Adler & Kamel, 2004; Grudzen, 2008). Volumes 1 and 2 focus on clinically relevant, ethnic-specific information about elders and their families in 15 different ethnic populations, and the third volume focuses on religious and spiritual issues for elders from 10 different traditions relevant to geriatric clinicians. The volumes, in particular, are used extensively by clinicians and educators as an on-demand resource because of the concise, compressed information oriented to practice that range from culturally appropriate ways to address an ethnic elder at the first clinical encounter to significant issues in the end-of-life phase and the dying process. Emphasis in all the volumes is on the heterogeneity of elders within the cultural and religious groups to try to reduce the tendency of students and providers to stereotype elders based on the compressed information.

Another valuable educational resource by a member of the AGS Ethnogeriatric Committee is the mnemonic developed by Fred Kobylarz, MD, "ETHNICS Mnemonic: A Clinical Tool for Ethnogeriatric Education" (Kobylarz, Heath, & Like, 2002). It includes seven parts of assessment of elders from diverse backgrounds with trigger questions for each, along with discussion of the process. It is available on the Florida State University School of Medicine Web site at http://www.med.fsu.edu/geriatrics/ethnogeriatric/module1/default.asp

Culturally Competent Gero-Nurse Online

The geriatric nursing Web site of the American Nurses Association (ANA, 2002), once known as GeroNurseOnline.org, was developed through the Nurse Competence in Aging Initiative funded by the Atlantic Philanthropies Inc. The award was channeled to the ANA through the American Nurses Foundation (ANF). It represents a strategic alliance between the ANA, the American Nurses Credentialing Center (ANCC), and the John A. Hartford Foundation Institute for Geriatric Nursing, New York University, College of Nursing, working with specialty nursing associations to incorporate a geriatric presence and enhance member competence in aging. Currently, the site has 29 geriatric learning modules for clinicians including a module titled "Ethnogeriatrics and Cultural Competence for Nursing Practice." The stand-alone modules are comprehensive, and nurses can receive continuing education units for some of the modules. This resource can be accessed at the new URL http://www.ConsultGeriRN.org

Articles in Professional Journals

Articles on ethnogerontology and ethnogeriatrics are often published in *The Gerontologist, Journal of Cross Cultural Gerontology, Journal of Gerontology, Journal of Gerontology and Geriatric Education, Journal of Gerontological Nursing,* and the *Journal of the American Geriatrics Society.* These resources provide a forum for scholarly interdisciplinary discussion of cultural, social, and health care issues involving different groups of people from diverse cultures and generations.

Books

A number of books are available that are used as textbooks in classes related to aging and diversity. Some that are especially of note are the following:

- *Worlds of Difference: Inequality in the Aging Experience* (3rd ed.), edited by Stoller and Gibson (2000). This is a volume of 44 vignettes, short stories, and reports of diverse elders from a wide variety of situations, circumstances, and backgrounds. It has been used extensively as a reader and as a trigger for discussion.
- *Aging and Diversity: An Active Learning Experience* (2nd ed.), by Mehrotra and Smith (2008), is designed as a textbook and includes content, cases, and student exercises that focus on various types of diversity, including socioeconomic status, religious affiliation, rural/urban differences, sexual orientation, and gender as well as race and ethnicity.
- A specialized book, *Understanding Elder Abuse in Minority Populations*, edited by Tatara (1999) is an excellent ethnogeriatric resource on a subject that continues to be denied, ignored, or culturally defined by groups of elders of color and their communities.
- *Ethnicity and the Dementias* (2nd ed.), edited by Yeo and Gallagher Thompson (2006), reviews the risks of dementia and issues and recommendations for assessment of cognitive status in different populations. Individual chapters on working with elders with dementia and their families are included for 12 specific ethnic populations and LGBT elders. It is appropriate for use as a text or reader for behavioral science and health care courses in aging, especially at the graduate level. A home study course for continuing education credit using the book as a text is being offered by Western Schools, especially for social work, psychology, and counseling providers.
- *Cultural Issues in End-of-Life Decision Making,* edited by Braun, Pietsch, and Blanchette (2000), includes ethnic and religious perspectives on death and dying and advanced directives, which would be helpful for educational programs in multiple health care disciplines.
- *Social Work Practice With the Asian American Elderly,* edited by Choi (2001), while written especially for social work education and practice, is relevant for programs in psychology and health care as well. The 10 chapters cover mental health, home health, long-term care and nutrition issues for elders in five different Asian American populations.

There are, of course, many times more than the number of resources mentioned in the preceding sections of this article that are related to cultural competence in general, such as the "National Standards for Culturally and Linguistically Appropriate Services in Health Care" developed by the Office of Minority Health (USDHHS & OMH, 2001). Faculty in gerontology and geriatrics have used many of these resources and adapted to their needs focusing on working with older adults.

CONCLUSION

Even with all the activity and growth of the fields of ethnogerontology and ethnogeriatric education described in this chapter, there are still major limitations. The availability of the training is still dependent heavily on the interest and expertise of individual faculty members. As noted in the responses to the AGHE survey, much of the instruction is integrated into other courses rather than stand-alone classes, thus it is vulnerable to the preferences of the faculty teaching those classes. Often, a faculty or an administration champion is essential to the survival of these courses.

Another limitation is the general lack of evaluation of approaches to teaching cultural diversity in aging. Although there have been individual efforts in individual programs, there is an absence of published literature that would provide evidence that ethnogerontological and ethnogeriatric education have resulted in positive effects on the trainees, their behavior or skills, or ultimately for older adults themselves. As the field matures, it is hoped this evidence can be produced.

REFERENCES

Adler, R. (Eds). (2006). *Doorway thoughts: Cross cultural care for older adults* (Vol. 2). Sudbury, MA: Jones and Bartlett.

Adler, R., & Kamel, H. (Eds.). (2004). *Doorway thoughts: Cross-cultural health care for older adults* (Vol. 1). Boston, MA: Jones and Bartlett.

American Nurses Association. (2002). *Nurse competency on aging.* Retrieved February 15, 2008, from http://consultgerim.org/topics/ethnogeriatrics_and_cultural_competence_for_nursing_prctice/want_to_know_more

Applewhite, S. & Torres, C.C. (2004). *Hispanic/Latino gerontology.* AGHE Brief Bibliography, Diversity Topics in Aging. Washington, DC: Association of Gerontology in Higher Education.

Asian Pacific Fund, AARP, & Stanford GEC. (2003). *Healing the spirit: Treatment of depression among the Asian elderly* [Educational video]. San Francisco, CA. Retrieved February 15, 2008, from http://www.asianpacificfund.org/resources/healthvideo.shtml

Braun, K. L., Pietsch, J. H., & Blanchette, P. L. (2000). *Cultural issues in end-of-life decision making.* Thousand Oaks, CA: Sage.

Choi, N. G. (2000). *Social work practice with the Asian American elderly.* New York: Haworth Press.

Cultural Competencies Writing Group. (2004). Curricular framework: Core competencies in multicultural geriatric care recommendations of the UC Academic Geriatric Resource Program and the Ethnogeriatrics Committee of the American Geriatrics Society. *Journal of the American Geriatrics Society, 52,* 137–141.

Federal Interagency Forum on Aging Related Statistics. (2000). *Older Americans 2000: Key indicators of well-being.* Hyattsville, MD: Author.

Francis, D., Shenk, D., & Sokolovsky, J. (1990). *Teaching about aging: Interdisciplinary and cross-cultural perspectives.* Washington, DC: Association for Anthropology and Gerontology.

Gelfand, D. E. & Kutzick, A. J. (Eds). (1979). *Ethnicity and Aging: Theory, Research, and Policy, Volume 5 in the Springer Series on Adulthood and Aging.* New York: Springer.

Grudzen, M. (Ed.). (2008). *Doorway thoughts: Cross cultural care for older adults (Spiritual and Religious Diversity)* (Vol. 3). Sudbury, MA: Jones and Bartlett.

Harper, M. (1990). *Minority aging: Essential curricula content for selected health and allied health professions.* Health Resources and Services Administration, Department of Health and Human Services. DHHS Publication No. HRS (P-DV-90–4). Washington, DC: U.S. Government Printing Office.

Jackson, J. J. (1976). Race, national origin, ethnicity, and aging. In R. H. Binstock & E. Shanas (Eds.), *Handbook of aging and the social sciences.* New York: Van Nostrand Reinhold.

John, R. (2004). *American Indian Aging.* AGHE Brief Bibliography, Diversity Topics in Aging. Washington, DC: Association of Gerontology in Higher Education.

Klein, S. (1996a). *A national agenda for geriatric education: Forum report.* Washington, DC: Health Resources and Services Administration.

Klein, S. (1996b). Ethnogeriatrics. In *A National Agenda for Geriatric Education: White Papers.* Washington, DC: Health Resources and Services Administration.

Kobylarz, F. A., Heath, J. M., & Like, R. C. (2002). The ETHNICS mnemonic: A clinical tool for ethnogeriatric education. *Journal of the American Geriatrics Society, 50,* 1582–1589.

McBride, M. (2006). *HRSA funded GECs' programs: Geriatric emergency preparedness training programs and resources.* Presentation at the 2006 Annual Meeting of the American Geriatrics Society, May 6, 2006, Chicago, IL.

McBride, M. (2008). *Ethnogeriatric teaching tools.* Presentation at the HRSA's Bureau of Health Professions All Programs Meeting, February 25–27, 2008, Washington, DC.

McBride, M., & Napier-Tibere, B. (2004). Harnessing technology and collaboration for an online ethnogeriatric educational resource. In A. Johnson, M. McBride, &

K. Hyer (Eds.), *Gerontology and Geriatrics Education, Vol. 24, No. 4*, 61–74. New York: Haworth Press.

Mehrotra, C., & Smith, L. (2008). *Aging and diversity: An active learning experience* (2nd ed.). New York: Routledge.

Nusberg, C. & Sokolovsky, J. (2004). *International aging*. AGHE Brief Bibliography, Diversity Topics in Aging. Washington, DC: Association of Gerontology in Higher Education.

Peterson, D. A., Bergstone, D., & Lobenstine, J. (1987). *National directory of educational programs in gerontology*. Washington, DC: Association for Gerontology in Higher Education.

Shenk, D. & Sokolovsky, J. (2004). *Cultural perspectives on aging*. AGHE Brief Bibliography, Diversity Topics in Aging. Washington, DC: Association of Gerontology in Higher Education.

Stoller, E. P., & Gibson, R. C. (2000). *Worlds of difference: Inequality in the aging experience* (3rd ed.). Thousand Oaks, CA: Pine Forge Press.

Tatara, T. (Ed.). (1999). *Understanding elder abuse in minority populations*. Philadelphia, PA: Brunner/Mazel—Taylor & Francis Group.

U.S. Department of Health and Human Services & Office of Minority Health. (2001). *National standards for culturally and linguistically appropriate services in health care, executive summary*. Retrieved February 15, 2008, from http://www.omhrc.gov/assets/pdf/checked/executive.pdf

Valle, R. (Ed.). (1976). *A cross-cultural study of minority elders in San Diego*. San Diego, CA: The Campanile Press, San Diego State University.

Whitfield, K. E. & Crowther, M. R. (2004). *Ethnogerontology and African Americans*. AGHE Brief Bibliography, Diversity Topics in Aging. Washington, DC: Association of Gerontology in Higher Education.

Yee, B. & Yeo, G. (2004). *Asian American and Pacific Islander Elders*. AGHE Brief Bibliography, Diversity Topics in Aging. Washington, DC: Association of Gerontology in Higher Education.

Yeo, G. (1988). *Review of current ethnogeriatric curriculum* (SGEC Working Paper Series, No. 2). Stanford, CA: Stanford Geriatric Education Center.

Yeo, G. (1989). *Ethnogeriatrics: Models and materials for geriatrics education in a multicultural context*. Presentation at the Annual Meeting of the Association for Gerontology in Higher Education. February 6–9, 1989, Tampa, FL.

Yeo, G., (1990). Review of ethnogeriatric curriculum development. In M. Harper (Ed.), *Minority aging: Essential curricula content for selected health and allied health professionals* (pp. 33–41). Washington, DC: U.S. Department of Health and Human Services.

Yeo, G. (1992). Ethnogeriatric curriculum and training in geriatric education centers. *Gerontology and Geriatrics Education, 12*, 3–7.

Yeo, G. (1993). Ethnogeriatric education: Need and recommendation. In *Shortage of health care professionals caring for the elderly: Recommendations for change* (pp. 75–88). Washington, DC: House Select Committee on Aging.

Yeo, G. (Ed.). (2004). *Mental health aspects of diabetes in elders from diverse populations.* Stanford, CA: Stanford Geriatric Education Center, Stanford University.

Yeo, G., & Gallagher Thompson, D. (2006). *Ethnicity and the dementias* (2nd ed.). New York: Taylor and Francis/Routledge.

CHAPTER 8

Lifelong Learning in Aging Societies

Emerging Paradigms

Ronald J. Manheimer

Learning opportunities for midlife and older adults have proliferated around the world since the early 1970s. We can attribute this growth to one or all of the following: (a) national efforts to promote lifelong learning societies for people of all ages, (b) initiatives responding specifically to sharp increases in the percentage of a country's older citizens, and (c) outgrowth of the adult and continuing education movement that gained momentum in the 19th century with the rise of democratic attitudes towards the benefits of education for all—including a nation's older citizens (Manheimer, 2007). Support for learning in later life can also be traced to the contributions of gerontological researchers who point to the value of fostering intellectual, emotional, and spiritual development that adds to the individual's quality of life and enhance his or her capacity for making social contributions. This life-course perspective underscores the mature adult's need and ability to adapt to situations that arise in mid- and later life such as the changing roles that may follow full or partial disengagement from the workforce, pursuit of postretirement careers, availability of more leisure time for creative ventures, and increased involvement in volunteer activities.

Growth of older learner programs can only be partially attributed to the academic field of gerontology, the activities of adult education organizations,

DOI: 10.1891/0198-8794.28.111

or the initiative of government agencies. In the United States, rather than a concerted national effort, the rise of older learner programs has been a grassroots phenomenon nurtured by a number of small groups and visionary leaders operating, at least initially, at the local level. Consequently, the United States lacks a central coordinating body. The various programs depend heavily on the services of volunteers and draw from a multiplicity of funding streams (e.g., from program fees, gifts, foundation grants, and occasionally public funding). One could argue that, for the United States, older learner programs play a marginal role relative to both academic gerontology and adult education, and that neither field has captured the dramatic emergence of this movement.

The strength of programs on the U.S. scene is their diversity, relative autonomy, and divergent creativity. Their weaknesses lie on the flip side: each has to fend for itself and justify its existence, its leaders are somewhat isolated from peers operating in different types of host organizations, and the programs are subject to the uncertainties of being marginally positioned in such organizations as universities, not-for-profit businesses, public libraries, museums, and trade unions. In other countries, by contrast, education for mature adults is largely a governmental matter, usually belonging to the portfolio of ministries of education.

To appreciate the current status of lifelong learning, it is imperative to understand the tangled web of mandates and goals, policies, and institutional motivations. Older learner programs have multiple origins, are influenced by dominant national ideologies concerning culture, education, retirement, and aging, and by the country's economic systems. In all cases, the older learner movement is an outgrowth of the unprecedented demographic rise of aging societies characterized by lengthened life expectancy, low birth rates, improved health care and hygiene, rising completion rates of postsecondary education, and relative affluence derived from public and private pensions funds. These factors, in turn, have contributed to an extension of midlife activity levels into people's 60s and 70s, in this way expanding the number of years encompassed by what is commonly called the Third Age (Laslett, 1991).

Additionally challenging to the student of older adult education is the field's continuing dynamic, driven by paradigm shifts that may gradually transform older learner programs into age-integrated or age-neutral educational programs. As members of the U.S. boomer generation pursue continued learning but resist identification with aging and the elderly, existing programs will have to refresh their images and public identities and perhaps the contents of their programs and how the programs are delivered. In this sense, older learner programs are headed toward an identity crisis. To understand why lifelong learning can be considered what sociologists call a "contested site," whose meaning is unstable and its future uncertain, we need to examine the institutional rationales for older learner programs, the motives of older learners themselves, how the two are expressed through a variety of exemplary programs hosted by diverse organizations, and how, with its great size and diversity, the aging boomer population may influence the next stages of this movement.

In what follows, we focus mainly on the older learner scene in the United States and its social context but refer to developments in other countries when these provide useful contrast.

WHY EDUCATION OF OLDER LEARNERS?

Education, as pioneering French sociologist Emil Durkheim told his students in 1902, "is the means by which society perpetually recreates the conditions of its very existence" (Durkheim, 1956, p. 123). Through formal schooling, the young learn the skills, values, and socially accepted behaviors that prepare them to be good citizens, productive workers, and, in many societies, to achieve personally fulfilling lives. Through their educational institutions, societies perpetuate themselves. And when societies change because of wars, social upheavals, or technological transformations—for example, the Vietnam War, the civil rights and women's movements, and digital technology and the Internet—then educational institutions must adapt accordingly and, hopefully, take on new leadership roles. This process of institutional revitalization is rarely immediate. As famed American educational philosopher John Dewey long ago pointed out, there is often a lag between changing social conditions and the ability of educational institutions to respond (Dewey, 1916).

What then about education for the not so young? In most postindustrial societies, adults beyond traditional secondary or postsecondary school age (18 and 25, respectively) may choose or sometimes be required to enroll in trade schools, continuing professional education or corporate training programs, or they may seek to pursue postgraduate degrees. In the United States, for example, it is increasingly common for working-age adults to pursue continuing education. According to the National Center for Educational Statistics (NCES), over one-third of adults aged 25–54 enrolled in some kind of work-related formal educational course in the academic year 2004–2005 (NCES, 2006).

What about people who are winding down careers or who have retired? Does society continue to have a stake in their further education, or are they now, on their own, free of social obligations and norms and, therefore, no longer the concern of national governments?

If the latter view were the case, then it would be difficult to understand why the Japanese Ministry of Education promoted the Lifelong Learning Act of 1990 to expand the number of Elder Colleges across that country as part of a plan to foster a lifelong learning society (Ministry of Education, Culture, Sports, and Technology, 2005) or why the Spanish Ministry of Education has supported the establishment of 47 Older Adult University Programs (OAUP) since the early 1990s (Bru Ronda, 2007). Generally speaking, these elder learning programs are not designed to help people retrain to reenter the labor force or to be better citizens. So, Professor Durkheim might ask, what socially viable end do they serve? To answer this question, we need to look at the types of organizations providing these educational opportunities.

The French government encourages people 50 and over to join Universities of the Third Age (U3As), based at state-supported institutions of higher learning and drawing on an academic faculty. U3As were started in France in 1973 as part of a governmental initiative aiming to expand university outreach to its citizens. Since then, hundreds of French-style U3As have cropped up across Europe with a sprinkling in French-speaking Canada and in the United States. A movement with the same name initiated in the United Kingdom in 1981 explicitly rejected university affiliation and eschewed government support. In the latter case, the British U3A members educate one another through topic-based learning circles in which they take turns presenting their research. Meeting in members' homes and local community centers, they take responsibility for teaching and for the organizational work of sustaining their groups. Britain, since the early 1960s, has its related public access educational effort in the form of the television, and now also Internet-based, Open University. This single example of the U3As indicates that there are different views about who should take responsibility for continued learning opportunities for older adults.

In France and other European countries and Japan, national and regional governments play major roles in managing lifelong learning for people of all ages, and institutions of higher education strongly influence their curricula and pedagogy. In the United Kingdom, older citizens have taken this authority for themselves.

In the case of the United States, where a Lifelong Learning Act was passed in 1976, only to fail to secure the appropriation of Congressional funding, there is a remarkable array of learning opportunities for midlife and older adults, some affiliated with public institutions such as colleges and universities (e.g., lifelong learning institutes or LLIs) and others operating through nonprofit organizations (e.g., the travel-learning program, Elderhostel, Inc.), or even stemming from for-profit businesses (e.g., The May Company department store's support for the Older Adult Services and Information Systems [OASIS] centers). Like its own economy, the lifelong learning business in the United States is a laissez-faire enterprise.

There must be some way to account for these diverse scenarios, each hinting that there is a multitude of compelling roles for education to play in the lives of older people. Discussing the Japanese situation, J. D. Wilson (2001) offers some helpful hints. According to Wilson, the list of government rationales for support of lifelong learning programs for midlife and older adults includes: enabling older adults to maintain a sense of purpose in their nonworking years, preserving and fostering cultural practices, acquiring new knowledge and skills to keep pace with and adapt to social changes, and reducing the physical care needs of aging citizens through teaching them about disease prevention and good self-care practices. In addition, the fact that the government takes an interest in the welfare of its aging citizens through supporting continued learning opportunities also helps to enhance their social status by communicating the social and cultural message that continued development throughout the life-course is important.

Wilson's list is insightful and accurately reflects a governmental viewpoint that would translate across many cultural borders into other countries in which a so-called graying of society is occurring. However, a governmental viewpoint is not necessarily identical with the outlook and motivation of older learners themselves. Government rationales for support of older learner programs tend to emphasize pragmatic goals such as lowering the state's burden for health care cost, ameliorating premature institutionalization, and mollifying mature voters to accept their new station in life (especially those who have been involuntarily shunted out of the labor force by downsizing or mandated retirement ages). Even a rationale currently in vogue in the United States, that continued cognitive challenge through various forms of education and the arts can delay or even prevent the onset of dementia (Cohen, et al., 2007), may receive a nod from government budget officers and even health care insurers. It may also prompt some mature adults to sign up for lifelong learning programs as a preventative health measure. But it is unlikely that adaptation to retirement, "brain health" or "cognitive benefits" would be an older learner's chief motive. Indeed, learner motives and government or host-institution rationales often differ.

Researchers have clustered motives for participating in lifelong learning into two broad categories: instrumental and expressive (Londoner, 1978). Instrumental motives have an extrinsic, in-order-to-achieve, character and include mastering certain skills such as playing an instrument, learning a foreign language, gaining facility with computer software applications, or acquiring budget management techniques. Expressive motives, sometimes deemed intrinsic, learning-for-its-own-sake, include deepening a sense of meaning, gaining insight into one's past, developing appreciation for art or music or literature, finding a voice through poetry or song, and seeking inner calm and insight through learning to meditate. Clearly, the two categories overlap, as one might pursue a life review process in order to write an autobiography, or might study Italian or Spanish as part of a planned trip to a country of origin in search of deepening one's sense of cultural heritage.

In addition to instrumental and expressive motives for pursuing continued learning, older learner programs share a common heritage with adult education, that of the camaraderie of one's fellow students. The social value of adult education can be traced to Benjamin Franklin's informal Junto, a small group of citizens that gathered monthly to present essays to one another on a wide variety of topics and who shared a meal and mutual support in the process. A hallmark of many older learner programs, even one's that are online, is the opportunity to widen one's circle of friends and to establish new relationships through the affinities of shared interest.

Confirming and expanding this perspective on older learner motives, Lamb and Brady (2005) found intellectual stimulation, participation in a supportive group, enhanced self-esteem, and opportunities for spiritual renewal to be the chief benefits expressed by mature students. Still, learner motives vary depending on whether participants are mainly involved in instrumental or expressive type programs.

Rationales for older learner programs, as we have seen, vary from country to country and from one host institution to another. The goals pursued by older learners are also diverse, ranging from acquiring specific skills to enriching personal growth and social networking. By highlighting a number of specific programs, primarily on the American scene, we can better understand how this movement is being played out.

EXEMPLARY PROGRAMS

College and university-based LLIs arose in the mid-1970s in part influenced by a prototype, the Institute for Retired Professionals (IRP), established in 1962 at the New School for Social Research (now New School University) in New York City. The IRP invited individuals seriously interested in intellectual subjects and willing to join small study circles based on specific scholarly pursuits to which they would contribute in turn. Over a decade would pass before a handful of similar member-led educational programs appeared by the mid-1970s (Manheimer, Snodgrass, & Moskow-McKenzie, 1995). But by the mid-1980s there was a sharp rise in the rate of new programs started each year until, by 2007, there were more than 400 of these programs across the United States and Canada, almost all linked with colleges and universities. Diverging from the British and French approaches, many of the American LLIs use an expert-led format rather than collaborative study circles and often draw on members as volunteer instructors or facilitators (Manheimer, 2005).

LLIs are unique not only because members are partially or fully in charge (host institutions may provide space and some clerical support) but because they are based on a financial model that requires participants, besides providing free labor and leadership, to help pay for a portion of the cost of their own continuing education. This financing method may seem unexceptional, but at the time of the model's inception, the idea that older learners should pay some portion of the cost of their own education was unprecedented. Previously, most older learner programs were free and generally depended on the largesse of private and public foundations and government subsidies. That earlier funding basis explains why programs were so often episodic, coming and going in repetitive cycles of "demonstration projects" that left no infrastructure behind. Perhaps the self-financing business model of most continuing education departments influenced LLIs where, institutionally, they are most often organizationally situated.

Today, the network of LLIs is loosely linked through affiliation with the Elderhostel Institute Network (EIN), a consortium supported, in part, through the largesse of Boston-based, Elderhostel (more about which will follow in this section). EIN makes available an extensive Web site that lists member programs in the United States and Canada, posts monthly newsletters, and provides extensive material on curricula, by-laws, how to start an LLI, and so on.

A second, newly emerging network of LLIs derives from the beneficence of the Bernard Osher Foundation, which has generously funded 117 Osher Lifelong Learning Institutes (or OLLIs), some of which are completely new and others remodeled and expanded versions of existing programs. OLLIs meet annually at a national conference, share a scholarly and informational journal, and gain the benefit of cross-fertilization and program sharing through a national coordinating office based at the University of Southern Maine.

During this same fertile period that saw the rise of LLIs, we find initiation of a lifelong learning component in the faith-based, volunteer-run Shepherd's Centers. Nonprofit community organizations sponsored by a coalition of religious congregations, Shepherd's Centers are committed to the delivery of services and programs for older adults. In 1972, the first Shepherd's Center was founded by Dr. Elbert C. Cole in Kansas City, Missouri. Twenty-three churches and synagogues joined in an interfaith effort to provide a ministry by, with, and for older adults. Today, over 75 Shepherd's Centers in 21 states comprise a network of 15,000 volunteers serving over 175,000 older adults. The services and programs of the Shepherd's Centers are designed to empower older adults to lead creative, productive, meaningful, and interdependent lives.

One of the many programs offered by the Shepherd's Centers is the Adventures in Learning program, which utilizes older adults as both teachers and students, planners and participants. Classes are normally held weekly, biweekly, or monthly. The purpose of the educational program is to provide an environment where older adults may share their knowledge, talents, skills, and new interests with their peers. A committee of volunteers makes the program decisions regarding curriculum, faculty, marketing, and evaluating. This committee is composed of faculty and students with backgrounds in education, public relations, administration, the arts, health, and clerical services. Most of the teachers are older adults who volunteer their time, knowledge, and skills.

OASIS is a consortium between business and not-for-profit organizations designed to challenge and enrich the lives of adults 50 and older. Educational, cultural, health, and volunteer outreach programs are offered at the OASIS Centers to provide participants an opportunity to remain independent and active in community affairs. In 1982, The May Department Stores Company, the original major national sponsor, provided OASIS with dedicated meeting and activity space in many of its stores. Initial support for the program was provided by the Administration on Aging. In 2005, Federated Department Stores bought out The May Company and inherited the OASIS program, which it continues to support in partnership with BJC HealthCare.

The OASIS national office establishes program quality requirements and overall management and operations guidelines. Currently there are 27 OASIS Centers operating from coast to coast with over 360,000 members. Each center has permanent and specially designed space for offices, student lounges, and meeting rooms. Courses are offered in areas of visual arts, music, drama, creative writing, contemporary issues, history, science, exercise, and health. Many courses are held in collaboration with local medical, cultural and educational institutions.

Volunteer outreach is an important component of the OASIS program. Many participants are trained in the Older Adult Peer Leadership (OAPL) program to teach classes in the community and to work in intergenerational programs helping young children. In 2006, more than 9,200 volunteers gave over 550,000 hours of their time to run the OASIS sites.

As an aside, it is worth noting that the name OASIS was originally used as an acronym for Older Adult Services and Information Systems, but, as with many organizations seeking to avoid aging stereotypes and sound less like a social service agency, it changed the name to just OASIS though it still uses a tag line that reads: "Enriching the lives of mature adults."

In 1986, SeniorNet, based in San Francisco and with initial support from the Markle Foundation, was established to encourage older learners to discover the benefits of computer-based information, communication, and the creative use of computer software. Subsequently, over 240 SeniorNet centers have cropped up in senior centers, public libraries, within LLIs, and in some retirement communities. SeniorNet sites also exist in other countries.

During the 1970s, with funding and mandates based on the Older Americans Act, the multiservice senior center concept began to flourish. Activities and services available at approximately 15,000 local, city, and county-funded centers included hot meals and nutritional education, health education, employment services, transportation assistance, social work services, educational activities, creative arts programs, recreation, leadership, and volunteer opportunities. The recreation–education component of senior center programming varies with availability of community resources and interests of participants. Some of the more common activities include arts and crafts, nature studies, science and outdoor life, drama, physical activity, music, dance, table games, special social activities, literary activities, excursions, hobby or special interest groups, speakers, lectures, movies, forums, round tables, and community service projects.

No sampler of lifelong learning programs should fail to include one of the longest established and most successful, Elderhostel, Inc. Launched in 1975 at the University of New Hampshire as an inexpensive, week-long campus summer residency program for people 55 and over, Elderhostel grew quickly and spread throughout colleges and universities in the United States and then abroad. The results of collaboration between maverick educator Marty Knowlton and university administrator David Bianco, Elderhostel typifies those lifelong learning ventures launched without any serious feasibility study and rather through the visionary leadership of a couple of innovative individuals.

Initially intended as a travel-learning program that might provide a taste of college-level intellectual life to those who had not been able to or could not afford to attend college, the program has mainly attracted college graduates (a large percentage of whom are either former teachers or spouses of teachers).

What began as a modest experiment with a social mission, Elderhostel quickly turned into a big business requiring a telephone call-in center and, later, on-line registration technology and a marketing and research division. Because Elderhostel now has many competitors, it must strive to update its image in order to attract a new generation of increasingly sophisticated and discriminating consumers. In 2004, Elderhostel launched Road Scholar, a set of more physically challenging, smaller group tours designed to attract a somewhat younger midlife population. Additionally, Elderhostel has undertaken a number of market research studies that provide insight into current and future participant attitudes.

The goal of a 2005 Elderhostel study was to determine into what categories a representative national sampling of people age 55 and over might be grouped in terms of attitudes toward health (mental and physical), mental stimulation, and lifelong learning activities. Two groups, whose attributes were summarized by the labels "Focused Mental Achievers" and "Contented Recreational Learners," were found to compose 47% of those surveyed while "Anxious Searchers," "Isolated Home Bodies," and "Pessimists" made up the rest. When a similar survey was directed toward former Elderhostel participants and 2,311 responses were analyzed, it turned out that 49% and 35%, respectively, fell into these first two categories (Elderhostel, 2007). That was fortunate for the multimillion-dollar nonprofit business because these two categories predict those individuals who are likeliest to sign up for continued learning opportunities. Moreover, Elderhostel researchers predict that these two (for them) favorable psychographic groupings will be even more highly represented among members of the boomer generation that is just easing its way into the retirement years.

The education and performing art scene is as extensive and lively as in other types of older learner programs. Hundreds of mature adult performing arts groups are listed in *Senior Theatre Connections* (Vorenberg, 1999), testifying to the international popularity of older person's participation in the arts and in intergenerational arts activities. In addition, the National Center for Creative Aging (NCCA) hosts a creative arts and aging network that includes programs in scores of major cities across the United States. In 2007, together with the New Jersey Performing Arts Center, NCCA published *Creativity Matters: The Arts and Aging Toolkit* to help groups across the United States and abroad to design, implement, and evaluate professionally led senior arts programs.

In many states, as part of the highly popular senior games, an Olympics-like sports competition for people 55 and over, there is a Silver Arts component encouraging everyone from painters to dancers to weavers to cheer leading teams to enter the competition and show their stuff.

This sampler is meant to indicate the range and types of programs that came to fruition in the United States over the past 40 years. It reveals that the lifelong learning movement that seeks to attract midlife and older adults has transformed itself from operating in a social service framework (providing leisure time activities for the "deserving elderly") to one that is more entrepreneurial—part of what Harry R. Moody calls the "silver industry" (Moody, 2004–2005).

To this array of programs, we must add other host sites, such as at community colleges, the YMCA and YWCA, Jewish community centers, art museums, hospital, and trade unions that have attracted large numbers of people in their 50s, 60, and 70s to partake in educational opportunities not specifically targeted to people by age or stage of life, or at least not identified as such. State legislation, mainly initiated in the early 1970s, has enabled thousands of citizens above a designated age (usually 65 but sometimes 62) to attend regular college and university classes on a tuition-free, space-available basis. Work-related educational programs sponsored by major companies constitute another large resource for people in midlife as part of retraining, upgrading of technical and managerial skills, and to a lesser extent as part of preparation for retirement. According to the NCES, 27% of people aged 55–64 and 5% of those 65 and over took work-related courses in 2005 (NCES, 2007).

COGNITIVE GYMNASTICS, BRAIN-MAINTAINING ARTS, AND PHYSICAL CULTURE

A number of surveys have indicated that of health concerns, besides losing their youthful looks, ballerina-like balance, and somewhat questionable memory capacity, a majority of baby boomers fear that they may eventually become demented or, worse, a victim of Alzheimer's disease. In response, a whole new industry has cropped up. Emphasizing a recent revision in neurological assumptions, researchers now report that the brain does, indeed, continue to produce new brain cells and dendrite connectivity. Consequently, the old "use it or lose it" adage, now scientifically supported, has helped create a multimillion-dollar industry of computer-based cognitive retraining programs designed to improve memory functions, linguistic, mathematical and spatial problem-solving abilities, and even hand-eye coordination. These cognitive retraining and enhancement programs are frequently marketed through language drawing from the world of physical fitness (e.g., "mental gymnastics"). While the exercise programs are not themselves educational in the narrow sense of the word, they do provide learning opportunities and purportedly function, by analogy, as adjunctive to intellectual activities as are strength training regimens to the playing of sports.

Besides these computerized retraining programs, many other activities, ranging from crossword puzzle solving to learning to play an instrument or to speak a foreign language, are touted as helping to keep the mind sharp. The American Society on Aging annually awards a MindAlert prize to programs that demonstrate a contribution to promoting mental acuity.

The great emphasis on lengthening midlife as long and far as possible is certainly an admirable one even if it is partially driven by a fear of death and a rejection of whatever people imagine it is to grow old. That there are many techniques and resources for slowing aging, even if, currently, most do not meet strict standards of scientific verifiability, will no doubt add to the attractiveness of lifelong learning activities (Salthouse, 2006). A few programs actually hint at or directly state that participation in their program could impede the aging process and contribute to brain health.

So it is not surprising that pragmatic reasons have been given for older persons' participation in the arts. Gene Cohen, for example, has headed up a 2-year creativity and aging study that, with the use of multiple sites and control groups, has demonstrated positive health advantages of activities, such as singing in choirs, that reduce visits to doctors' offices, lower use of medicines, help to offset depression, and generally add to older persons' quality of life (Cohen, et al., 2007). These positive results, Cohen underscores, contribute to reducing health care costs that society must shoulder. This utilitarian rationale for older persons' participation in the arts and in other forms of lifelong learning may attract government support and that of the health care and insurance industries.

The problem with utilitarian justifications for lifelong learning is that they can distract from the intrinsic value and pleasure of these activities, even further extending the medical model of aging into realms formerly safe from health outcome measures. Many intellectual, cultural, and artistic activities would lose their appeal were they tainted by the odor of disinfectant and the clinical seal of approval as contributing to mental alertness. This, however, may be a matter of packaging because one can use a certain vocabulary and set of rationales for obtaining research and grant money and another for inducing people to sign up for programs.

Our third category, physical fitness, is also a burgeoning industry, with health clubs, spas, fitness centers, and seniors sport leagues growing by leaps and bounds while new books, magazines, and Web sites spring up to celebrate the benefits of proper diet, good balance, cardiovascular endurance, agility, flexibility and the corollary mental health benefits of physical robustness. Tai chi and yoga also have become highly popular with midlifers because they combine the benefits of balance and flexibility training with an aura of spiritual enhancement. Blended modalities such as "yogalates" (yoga plus Pilates) may offend the purists who worry that mixing modalities distorts the central purposes of either martial arts forms or traditional spiritual movement practices. But in the true American spirit of the cafeteria approach to all things good and beneficial, these hybrids are sure to gain in popularity.

Again, should these types of exercises be included in lifelong learning? Indeed, what could be more valuable than gaining greater knowledge about one's body and skill in preserving or even improving its functionality? The "physical culture" (to use an old-fashioned expression befitting the architecture of some fitness centers that look more like temples than gyms) industry will continue to expand to meet the expectations of health-conscious boomers who, ironically, show higher rates of obesity, diabetes, and musculoskeletal ailments than that seen in their parents' generation.

FORECASTING THE FUTURE

Considering the near-term future, as a correlate to these trends, lifelong learning opportunities will increasingly become a function of the marketplace. Those who are in sufficiently good health, are motivated by having enjoyed prior years of education (the main predictor of participation), and can afford to enroll in LLIs, pay for travel-learning excursions, sign up for continuing education courses, register for back-to-campus alumni seminars, access Internet educational sites, and choose from among a cornucopia of other lifelong learning programs, will reap the benefits of "successful aging." Educational programming for baby boomers especially will be a thriving business that deans of continuing education programs and directors of for-profit travel-learning companies, among others, are (or should be) discovering. We should expect an increase in demand for vocational education for second and third careers with likely emphasis on technical, managerial, and business-related training needs. Also, retirement communities associated with colleges and universities should experience a surge in growth.

Those who do not fare so well because of poor health, limited incomes, lack of motivation because of more restrictive prior education (especially minority neo-elders), will find comparatively little from which to choose in the way of intellectually challenging programs. In fact, those who do not fit the image of successful aging will be chastised as somehow "failed agers," a moral castigation of those who seem not to have seized the opportunity to age well.

It doesn't require much reflection to see that this scenario is an extension of current trends.

Educational programs that hold onto the current nomenclature—self-identified as for elders, for retirees, for seniors—run the risk that they may age in place, mainly attracting a frailer, older population, a trend already occurring at some of the most popular Elderhostel sites such as the famous music conservatory, the Peabody Institute. The shift to age-neutral program names will not be enough to achieve organizational rebranding to capture the neo-elderly. The challenge for many programs will be how they retain a unique identity if they elect an age-neutral identity. Such programs have the added challenge of continuing to service their existing participants as they grow frailer and age in place.

Changes in pedagogical methods may also be critical to attract future lifelong learning students. Jean Sheridan (2007), an astute observer of current older learner programs, argues that unless these programs embrace more of a collaborative learning culture rather than the traditional expert-led, highly performance-oriented lecturer format that is currently popular with lifelong learning programs, they will find their participants aging in place. It is true that many university instructors have adopted teaching methods that focus on learners as problem-solvers operating in the context of a democratic classroom model. Whether this will translate into the lifelong learning movement for those in the second half of life remains to be seen.

Lifelong learning programs in the United States and Canada will continue to mirror their countries' economic systems. These programs—whether conducted through colleges, senior centers, hospitals, libraries, religious congregations, or sponsored by private sector organizations such as banks, department stores, and travel-learning agencies—will remain market driven and increasingly require full fees or some form of co-payment for enrollment.

Lifelong learning can be compared to that segment of the housing industry that caters to midlife and older adults. The entry of a large and diverse boomer population into the Third and Fourth Age will accelerate trends that are already occurring for more diverse types of housing. These niche markets include patio homes, age-qualified communities (both freestanding homes and condos), amenity-rich, concierge service condos and apartments, full-service retirement communities (continuing care or life care models), assisted-living facilities, university-linked retirement communities, retirement villages (health care being separate), and now the attention-getting virtual communities, such as Beacon Hill Village, in which older neighborhood resident pay fees for a concierge-based menu of home, health, and transportation services. In addition, we will see increased interest in both intergenerational and elder cohousing communities (tightly clustered villages that include commonly owned property and community centers equipped with kitchen and dining rooms for communal meals, and often with other such amenities as arts studios, meditation rooms, libraries, and so on depending on members' preferences).

Similarly, lifelong learning for midlife and older adults will accommodate both highly individualized, small group as well as traditional, large group ("windshield") travel-learning programs. Cooperative art studios that offer both training and studio space for practicing one's art or craft will grow dramatically, especially in towns with strong arts and crafts traditions and in college and university towns. Online courses offered by public and private universities and through a wide range of other vendors (libraries, art museums, online special interest type magazines) will greatly enhance the independent learner's range of resources. Academic programs at colleges and universities designed to enable midlife adults to "recareer" will also be popular as will certificate programs for both vocationally related and personal development—oriented learners. These certificate programs could qualify people for paraprofessional levels of involvement in social causes (e.g., the NC Center for Creative Retirement offers a Blue Ridge Naturalist certificate for those who seek to deepen their commitment to environmental causes) or to enter a postretirement career in, for example, real estate, accounting, biotechnology, child care, patient advocacy, or library work.

Some programs will disappear or be absorbed into existing administrative units of host organizations losing their previous age or life-stage designation, and other programs will find themselves lodged in appropriate spaces and more permanent buildings. If, as some predict, a majority of baby boomers scorn association with older age identified groups, preferring age-integrated activities and learning programs, then there will be a sharp fall out (or change of identity) of a good many programs. Opportunities for innovation in lifelong learning beckon the visionary individual and group who recognize the importance and value of continued learning in the later years. Representative of such forward thinking is the American Council on Education (ACE, 2007) that, with funding from the MetLife Foundation, is in the midst of a national study, "Reinvesting in the Third Age: Older Adults and Higher Education," a research project that anticipates the transformative role that educational institutions may play in helping create a broader vision for ours and other nations' aging societies.

REFERENCES

American Council on Education. (2007). *Framing new terrain: Older adults and higher education.* Washington, DC: Author.

Bru Ronda, C. (2007). Older Adult Education Programmes (OAUPs) in Spain: A socio-educational and political challenge in the context of lifelong learning. Proceedings, *A legacy of learning, Sharing global experiences of learning in later life* (pp. 28–38). Glasgow, Scotland: University of Strathclyde.

Cohen, G. D., Perlstein, S., Chapline, J., Kelly, J., Firth, K., & Simmens, S. (2007). The impact of professionally conducted cultural programs on the physical health, mental health, and social functioning of older adults—2 year results. *Journal of Aging, Humanities and the Arts, 1*(1–2), 5–22.

Dewey, J. (1916). *Democracy and education.* New York: The Macmillan Company.

Durkheim, E. (1956). *Education and sociology* (S. D. Fox, Trans.). Glencoe, IL: The Free Press.

Elderhostel, Inc. (2007). *Mental stimulation and lifelong learning activities in the 55+ population.* Retrieved September 29, 2008. from http://www.elderhostel.org/research/lifelonglearning/

Lamb, R., & Brady, E. M. (2005). *Participation in lifelong learning institutes: What turns members on?* Portland, ME: Osher Lifelong Learning Institute, University of Southern Maine.

Laslett, P. (1991). *A fresh map of life: The emergence of the third age.* Cambridge, MA: Harvard University Press.

Londoner, C. A. (1978). Instrumental and expressive education: A basis for needs assessment and planning. In R. H. Sherron & D. B. Lumsden (Eds.), *Introduction to educational gerontology* (2nd ed., pp. 85–106). Washington, DC: Hemisphere.

Manheimer, R. (2005). The older learner's journey to an ageless society: Lifelong learning on the brink of a crisis. *Journal of Transformational Education, 3*(3), 198–221.

Manheimer, R. (2007). Education and aging. In J. E. Birren (Ed.), *Encyclopedia of gerontology* (2nd ed., pp. 463–475). Amsterdam: Elsevier.

Manheimer, R., Snodgrass, D., & Moskow-McKenzie, D. (1995). *Older adult education: A guide to research, programs, and policies,* Westport, CT: Greenwood Press.

Ministry of Education, Culture, Sports, Science and Technology. (2005). *Lifelong learning and social education.* Retrieved October 15, 2007, from http://mext.jo.jp/english/org/eshisaku/eshougai/htm

Moody, H. R. (2004–05). Silver industries and the new aging enterprise. *Generations, 28*(4), 75–78.

National Center for Educational Statistics.(2006). *Adult education participation 2004–2005.* Retrived September 29, 2008, at http://nces.ed.gov/PUBSEARCH/pubsinfo.asp?pubid=2006077

National Center for Educational Statistics. (2007). *Educational participation among older adults: 2005. Enrollment in postsecondary institutions, fall 2005: First look.* Washington, DC: Government Printing Office.

Salthouse, T. A. (2006). Mental exercise and mental aging, evaluating the validity of the "use it or lose it" hypothesis. *Perspectives on Psychological Science, 1*(1), 68–87.

Sheridan, J. (2007). Lifelong learning in a post-modern age: Looking back to the future through the lens of adult education. *The LLI Review, 2,* 4–16.

Vorenberg, B. (1999). *Senior theatre connections: Senior theatre performing groups, professionals and resources.* Portland, OR: ArtAge Publications.

Wilson, J. D. (2001). Lifelong learning in Japan: A lifeline for a maturing society. *International Journal of Lifelong Learning, 20*(4), 297–313.

SECTION III

APPROACHES TO GERONTOLOGY EDUCATION AND APPLICATION

This section brings the theoretic approach to education in gerontology to practical, frontline considerations. It is led by a chapter by Robert Applebaum and Jesse Leek of Miami University titled "Bridging the Academic/Practice Gap in Gerontology and Geriatrics: Mapping a Route to Mutual Success." They argue that with the demographic imperative of the aging baby boom generation, the traditional separation between academic gerontology/geriatrics and aging services networks cannot be sustained. Resources in both settings are limited and cannot be expected to expand in keeping with the expansion of the population. They suggest a collaborative, partnership approach to education of future generations of gerontologists and geriatricians, giving examples of how this approach should be considered and structured.

The next chapter discusses the approach to the use of technological interventions in gerontology education. Donna M. Weinreich of Western Michigan University and Jennifer Mendez of Wayne State University authored the chapter titled "A Philosophical Foundation for Multimedia Design in Gerontology and Geriatrics." They reviewed the literature for evidence of systematic approaches to content design in virtual learning environments, and found it lacking. They thus present the seven principles of good practice, the psychological principles of learner-centered teaching, and Meyer's principles of multimedia design as a framework from which evaluation of the efficacy of multimedia instruction can be launched.

The third chapter in this section, by Judith L. Howe of Mt. Sinai School of Medicine, is titled "Education and Training of Community Health Professionals and Service Providers." Dr. Howe presents an overview of the current state of geriatric training and education programs for community health professionals and service providers. Included in her discussion are the rationale and goals of training, targeted disciplines, benefits of training, a survey of curriculum domains, and a description of training methods and settings. She also discusses sustainability issues and reviews future directions for dissemination of principles of geriatrics in the community.

The final chapter in this section, by Anthony A. Sterns of Creative Action LLC and Edward F. Ansello of Virginia Commonwealth University, is titled "Education About Special Aging Populations: Intellectually Disabled,

Incarcerated, and Non-English-Speaking." The authors discuss aging in three special populations: those with intellectual and developmental disabilities, those who are incarcerated, and limited or non-English-speakers in the United States. They note the parallels between these groups and opportunities for optimizing physical and mental health of these special populations. Lessons learned from these populations can potentially be applied to broader groups of elders.

CHAPTER 9

Bridging the Academic/Practice Gap in Gerontology and Geriatrics

Mapping a Route to Mutual Success

Robert Applebaum and Jessie Leek

The job of higher education in gerontology is to teach students about our aging society, to assist in developing a workforce to provide goods and services to this growing population, and to generate research and evaluation data that can improve programs and services. Despite a universal knowledge about the aging of our nation and an expansion of academic programs in gerontology and geriatrics, producing professionals to work with older people across the range of needed areas has proven to be difficult. Attracting adequate numbers of students to gerontology and geriatrics as practitioners or researchers, whether in nursing, social work, medicine, social service administration, or long-term care, has been a consistent issue of concern (Anderson, 1999; Blanchette & Flynn, 2001; Cummings & Adler, 2007). With the continued growth of the aging population, a different strategy will be required to expand the number of workers and researchers trained in gerontology and geriatrics.

The aging network, defined as the array of agencies that deliver social, health, income support, and long-term care to older people in the United States, has a responsibility to ensure that older people have access to and receive the necessary information and services. Gerontology and geriatrics

DOI: 10.1891/0198-8794.28.131

workforce shortages of today are combined with projections for a more than doubling of the over-65 population in the coming decades. Such projections indicate that the aging network, already limited in resources, will likely need to serve an increasingly greater number of older Americans, making efficiency and effectiveness of services an ever-growing issue of importance. In addition to the funding and quality challenges, the future delivery system for older people faces continued challenges regarding an adequate workforce to deliver the needed assistance.

It is clear that the difficulties faced by both higher education and the aging network in meeting the needs of an aging society are monumental. What is less clear is how the challenges can be addressed through a mutually beneficial and unified strategy. Although there are a number of examples of how higher education and the aging network can work together, these partnerships still appear to be pleasant aberrations rather than standard practice. It is the contention of this chapter that in order for both areas to thrive, such partnerships cannot be thought of as interesting innovations but rather must become part of the educational/practice paradigm in gerontology. The future needs of our aging society are so great that it is simply not possible for the aging network or gerontological higher education to succeed in the absence of such partnerships.

THE AGING NETWORK IS FROM MARS AND HIGHER EDUCATION IS FROM VENUS: BARRIERS TO SUCCESSFUL PARTNERSHIP ACTIVITIES

Despite considerable agreement that higher education and the aging network need to work together and evidence that such partnerships have generated important advantages for both sectors, examples of successful partnerships appear to be the exception rather than the rule. Why is this relationship, which seems like such a good idea for both groups, not more commonplace?

A review article by Cyert and Goodman (1997) suggest three major reasons why university/corporate partnerships are difficult to create and maintain. Although aging network providers are not typically the type of corporations referred to in this article, there are similarities that make this comparison applicable to gerontology.

First identified are the differences in organizational cultures, including differences in goals, time, language, and assumptions. For example, most companies operate on relatively short time frames, such as quarters, compared to the university, which tends to operate on a longer and less well-defined time frame. Universities often have difficulty responding to fast turnaround project requests. Also, the language of research is not always the common lexicon for nonuniversity organizations. There are different assumptions about how work is managed and performed. University researchers are often independent and have strong linkages to professional associations, while company staff members have primary allegiance to their organizations of employment.

A second area identified by Cyert and Goodman addresses differences in the nature of work and the outcomes it produces. For instance, companies typically look for tangible products with applied applications, while universities are more interested in generating innovative ideas and in the testing of new models and concepts. Again, the differences in time frame can also contribute to problems in this area.

The third area identified surrounds what Cyert and Goodman refer to as "exogenous shocks." Although the university world is not completely independent, in the past it has not been subject to the rapid management changes typically experienced in private organizations. For example, a change in management could mean less interest in the collaboration, and universities are typically much less likely to be affected by such changes than are private sector organizations.

The literature on the separation of research and practice is extensive. Interestingly, this literature reinforces the philosophical and pragmatic differences that exist between the two groups. For example, researchers writing in a well-known management journal began their article stating: "It is hardly news that many organizations do not implement practices that research has shown to be positively associated with employees productivity and firm financial performance" (Rynes, Giluk, Brown, 2007, p. 987). The assumption by these and other researchers is that substantial information is available to practitioners, who should be able to use evidence-based research results to improve their services or products. The authors seem to be surprised that the practice world does not take advantage of the available research provided by universities, and they directly or indirectly imply some failure on the part of the practice community.

Interestingly, the opposite concern has been expressed by those in the practice field who have argued that the issues of greatest importance to practitioners are not typically examined by researchers (Deadrick & Gibson, 2007). Researchers have also argued that there is often disagreement in study outcomes about what best practice actually includes, making it even more difficult for practitioners to apply research data to practice (Guest, 2007). Thus, each group perceives the other as unable to understand its needs, resulting in high levels of frustration and limited collaborations.

To supplement these general principles, we identify areas of difference directly applicable to the field of gerontology. First, because many of the aging network providers are funded by the public sector or private philanthropies, budgets are typically tight. Aging network agencies interested in partnering with universities are often shocked when they learn about the large negotiated overhead agreements charged for federal grants. University research offices in many instances are not willing to be flexible about such rates when it comes to local projects.

A second area involves differences in orientation and attitudes about the role of research and program evaluation. Service delivery professionals believe that the program or service provided by the agency is effective. In fact, as consumers we want our service providers to believe in their practice. University staff members are trained to question the effectiveness of programs and practices and often start out with skepticism about service effectiveness. Efforts to conduct research, particularly issues surrounding research design and data collection tools, often generate very different reactions for higher education and the aging network.

These culture differences, timing challenges, and differing perspectives on research can result in each side having a negative understanding of the other's view. For example, agency staff members feel that faculty and researchers in higher education do not have a good understanding of the real world. The criticism of academic staff involved in teaching and research is that they are not grounded, practical, or helpful. On the other hand, university personnel believe that aging network staff members are not taking advantage of the most up-to-date research and training resources and that they do not respect the research process.

Finally, both groups face time pressures in the context of limited funding. Although resource limitations are not unique to gerontological higher education or the aging network, they do present a real constraint. With more tasks than time, it is difficult to engage in an additional activity, particularly one in which the benefits are not clearly defined. Limited support in both of these areas makes the exploration of new partnerships a more difficult enterprise. The time frame to undertake and complete research activities is a related concern in this area. Higher education does not typically respond well to projects that require a quick turnaround, because commitments for the semester or academic year drive time allocation. Because aging network agencies operate in real time with real problems, the university calendar is often seen as not in tune with practice needs. On the other hand, university researchers express frustration because they feel that aging network agencies don't have an appreciation for the research process, including how long it takes to design and implement a sound research project.

Although these differences are real, a number of experiences across the nation highlight examples of successful collaborations. In some instances, these efforts are primarily the responsibility of higher education, in others, the aging network. and finally others truly reflect a partnership between the two. In the following sections we present an overview of the type of activities that currently exist, with an emphasis on successes and barriers. In the final section we discuss recommendations for improving collaborative efforts.

HIGHER EDUCATION ACTIVITIES WITH THE AGING NETWORK: FORMAL EDUCATIONAL PROGRAMS

One of the most basic goals of gerontological higher education is to produce a well-prepared workforce for our aging society. An important intersection of higher education and the aging network exists in the formal education programs that prepare individuals to work with older adults in some capacity. Formal higher education programs produce nurses, social workers, therapists, dieticians, health care administrators, physicians, policy and program planners, gerontologists, and others who serve older adults through their practice.

While it is the case that many currently working within the aging network may not have distinctly set out with career plans to do so, others have obtained their education with the expressed goal of serving elders. There is increasing public awareness about the growth of the older population; this is likely to increase expectations for higher education to prepare students to live and work in an aging world (Anderson, 1999).

The Association for Gerontology in Higher Education (AGHE) suggests there are three educational paths for those looking to work in the field of aging: (a) traditional disciplines with a specialized focus on aging, (b) gerontology, as a multidisciplinary or interdisciplinary approach, and (c) continuing education for those interested in nondegree programs (Peterson, Douglass, & Whittington, 2004). Those seeking degreed programs will find a range of associate-level through doctoral and postdoctoral work available. Gerontology programs at all levels have increased in number over the past several decades. Growth in graduate programs is seen as especially indicative of the increase in formal gerontology programs (Anderson, 1999). A recent review of gerontology programs revealed master's degrees offered at 57 universities and doctoral degrees offered at 9 universities in the United States (Haley & Zelinski, 2007).

Ironically, the increase in gerontology programs has occurred in a climate of relative uncertainty regarding the job market for gerontologists. Structural lag in the form of deeply ingrained disciplinary silos within academia and licensure requirements in service organizations can make it challenging for some gerontologists to find employment easily. Haley and Zelinski (2007) note a "context of traditional disciplinary research and professional training programs that dominate the landscape" (p. 25). Problematically, within these traditional disciplines and professional training programs there are an inadequate number of students choosing specializations or certifications in aging. For example, there is a shortage of geriatricians in our country (Blanchette & Flynn, 2001). The American Geriatrics Society reports there were 7,128 board-certified geriatricians as of April, 2007—a ratio of 1 geriatrician for every 2,546 Americans age 75 or older. This ratio is expected to change to 1:4,254 by the year 2030, because of the projected rapid increase in the number of older adults (The American Geriatrics Society, 2008).

Similarly, the professions of nursing and social work are experiencing worker shortages, and especially significant is the shortage of aging specialists within these two fields (Cummings & Adler, 2007; Robertson & Cummings, 1996). Efforts in both professions exist to increase the numbers of professionals in general, and also to increase the number of professionals choosing to practice within the field of aging. For example, in early 2008, the Dorothy I. Height/Whiney M. Young, Jr. Social Work Reinvestment Act was introduced in Congress with bipartisan support in an effort to promote recruitment, retention, research and reinvestment in the profession of social work.

Given what we know about our nation's demographic imperative, what are some possible hindrances in attracting sufficient numbers of students and workers to programs and professions that serve the needs of older adults? The pervasiveness of ageism within our country likely creates an aversion to a career in aging for some (Anderson, 1999; Cummings & Adler, 2007). Financial disincentives may also play a role in discouraging potential geriatric social workers and geriatricians (Lubben & Harootyan, 2002; The American Geriatrics Society, 2008). Interestingly, national organizations representing both social workers and geriatricians advocate for loan forgiveness policies as a strategy for increasing the number of professionals in these fields. Currently, only South Carolina has such a loan forgiveness program for recruiting geriatricians who agree to practice within the state for 5 years (The American Geriatrics Society, 2008).

Institutional structures themselves may also hinder the recruitment of students and future workers to careers in aging (Anderson, 1999; Haley & Zelinski, 2007; Lubben & Harootyan, 2007). By their very nature, institutions often lack flexibility and are generally unable to change direction quickly in response to market needs.

CONTINUING EDUCATION PROGRAMS

As discussed earlier in this chapter, the AGHE suggests that one educational path to employment in the field of aging is through continuing education. Continuing education may take the form of coursework, programs, or other types of formal learning experiences. Typically, continuing education programs are noncredit but may offer units necessary to maintain a license. In many cases, people seek out continuing education for the purpose of career advancement, career change, or personal enrichment.

Continuing education that ultimately benefits older adults through increases in and improvements to services are of mutual interest to higher education and the aging network. Higher education is involved through the development of curriculum, course and noncredit program offerings, and community partnerships with provider agencies. Continuing education can be important to those working with older adults as a way to keep current regarding the dynamic nature of aging-related work. For example, it is necessary to keep abreast of policy changes at the state and federal level, regulation changes, changing consumer expectations, research and technology developments, treatment and care best practices, and myriad other changes that occur within the field. Maybe even more fundamentally, continuing education is important because many providing social and health care services to older adults have not benefited from an adequate aging-related education (Langer, 1999).

Following, we describe several examples of programs developed through partnerships between higher education and service providers toward the ultimate goal of improving services to older adults. Specifically, a program to increase physician education in geriatrics, a program to provide gerontological knowledge to nurses, and a program to develop cross-professional partnerships between social workers and extension educators will be reviewed.

Addressing the need for greater geriatrics knowledge among generalist physicians, the Practicing Physician Education Project (PPE) was jointly created in 1997 through the efforts of the John A. Hartford Foundation of New York and the American Geriatrics Society. By utilizing a train-the-trainer model, nongeriatrician physician leaders were trained by expert faculty to offer continuing medical education (CME) employing adult learning techniques and tool kits of resources about specific geriatric-related topics. A description of the PPE is detailed in the *Journal of the American Geriatrics Society*. An evaluation of this project that used a 6-month follow-up revealed positive effects on both physicians' perceived knowledge and office-based practice for two of the tool kit topics, specifically memory loss and urinary incontinence (Levine et al., 2007). This program highlights a creative response to both the challenges of offering continuing education using pedagogy appropriate for adult learners and increasing knowledge about aging-related topics for those working with older adults but not trained in geriatrics or gerontology.

A similar train-the-trainer approach for nursing professionals was used in a partnership between the Social Gerontology Program at the University of the Incarnate Word in San Antonio and a Santa Rosa Health Care Network (Langer, 1999). Like the physicians' train-the-trainer program described previously, this program design addressed both gerontological content and pedagogy appropriate for adult learners. The collaboration between experts in higher education and professional nursing was considered an integral part of this continuing education offering. Advantages of such partnerships include opportunities for further research and program development, the chance for faculty to better understand practice contexts, and enhanced community exposure for both entities.

Another creative approach to continuing education can be found in a program developed by two North Carolina State University faculty members partnering across disciplines (Social Work and Family and Consumer Sciences) based on shared interest in gerontological education (Waites & Bearon, 2007). The program was designed as an institute offering gerontological knowledge content as well as skill development in program planning, case management, and resource utilization. Participants for the institute were recruited through social work agencies, county extension offices, and area agencies on aging. Application for participation required social worker/extension agent dyads with a program development idea for the community in which they both served. By pairing professionals from distinct disciplines, the institute cultivated interdisciplinary partnerships with the common goal of service to older adults and their families. Faculty reaching across disciplines and to the greater community in collaboration with professionals in the field of aging hold great promise for further leveraging our efforts to improve the lives of older adults.

Continuing education also has a very important role in the professional growth of direct care workers such as nurse aides and chore workers (Braun, Cheang, & Shigeta, 2005). However, there is limited research on continuing education effectiveness in long-term care. Increased research attention in this area holds further promise for partnerships between higher education and the aging network.

IN-SERVICES, BOARD SERVICE, AND OTHER CONSULTATION ACTIVITIES

A third area of involvement of educators involves support services for agencies. This includes a range of activities, from a staff training session about a new topic area to ongoing activities, such as being a board member or providing periodic consultation. These activities have the advantage of being useful to both the practitioner agency and as a valuable learning tool to the faculty. These arrangements also provide a jumping off point for future relationships between higher education and the practice world.

RESEARCH ACTIVITIES

There are numerous examples of university researchers conducting applied research and evaluation studies. Such projects are typically undertaken in one of three ways: (a) generated by a university research unit or a by a funder or regulator, (b) agency initiated as part of ongoing management activities, or (c) jointly developed through an agency/university collaboration.

The most common model is externally generated research efforts. In some instances such efforts might be driven by funder or regulatory requirements, while in others it may simply be that the university researchers are looking for a site to test, demonstrate, or evaluate a particular program or intervention. The gerontological literature, including such journals as the *Journal of Applied Gerontology* and the *Gerontologist,* contain numerous examples of this model. A review of the recent literature identified a wide range of studies that make an important contribution to the field. Almost all applied researchers, including the authors, have used this approach. Although this model can and does generate important knowledge for the field, it does not typically invite collaboration, participation, or buy-in from the practice setting. The most common criticism of these studies is that results are often not relevant to the practice organization. Agencies do not routinely report positive practice outcomes as a result of these types of studies. Findings from studies of this nature may result in publication, which, while beneficial to the researcher, does not necessarily prove useful in efforts to improve practice.

A second category includes research studies that are initiated by the practice organization. In some instances these are implemented through a request for proposal system in which monetary resources are available. In other cases, university researchers are asked to participate with little or no funding involved. Exchanges, such as accepting students in internship programs, may facilitate the relationship. Again, in many instances this model can generate research information that is deemed valuable to the agency. In some cases it can be used by an agency to request additional resources or to modify a program or policy. Such an effort could result in dissemination opportunities that are attractive for researchers.

Although this type of approach can generate mutually beneficial gains for both partners, it is not without common challenges. From the agency perspective, time frame is often a problem. Agencies typically need answers quickly in order to address real-time problems. Universities often have difficulty responding to immediate requests, because academic schedules are planned out a semester or year in advance. University researchers express frustration because agencies frequently underestimate the amount of time required to design, implement, analyze and write up a research study. A common criticism is that projects initiated by agencies do not include enough resources, and in many cases the time frame is not adequate.

The third classification includes projects that are developed collaboratively between practice organization and higher education. In this model, agency and university staff come together and jointly identify the research project to be developed. The research question, design, and data collection are discussed. Both groups shape the study, each lending its perspective and experience. Many of the issues that can result in frustration for both groups are discussed and negotiated at the front end of the project. Although such efforts are not the norm, this model does represent a path to mutually beneficial projects.

As an example we provide a brief description of a collaborative effort between our university and the local area agency on aging (Applebaum, Kunkel, & Wilson, 2007; Murdoch, Kunkel, Applebaum, & Straker, 2004). This project developed out of an ongoing relationship between the two entities that has developed over the past decade. The partnership began with a university-initiated project and now includes all three models. Periodic meetings are used to identify potential collaborative projects, and the project described is a result of one of those sessions. The collaborative effort combined the desire and need of the area agency to collect better consumer satisfaction information from the more than 5,000 participants in its home care program and researchers' desire to develop an improved approach to measuring and collecting satisfaction data from older consumers.

The project was complicated by the fact that the area agency contracted with more than 60 providers and wanted to be able to provide specific feedback to each provider about program performance. This meant that a large sample was needed, and thus the agency needed a cost-efficient data collection approach. The study examined whether program care managers, who had to make periodic home visits as part of the program intervention, could reliably collect satisfaction data as well. A test, re-test methodology using care managers and research interviewers was implemented, and findings showed that care managers could collect data reliably. This led the area agency to implement an agency-wide consumer satisfaction approach. Today, the agency issues a report to all providers, showing their consumer satisfaction score in comparison to the average of all other similar providers.

A variant of this approach has been community-based research partnerships. In these efforts a model is used in which a wide array of practitioners and researchers join together to both identify a practice area of interest and to develop a research approach (Sabir et al., 2006).

AGING NETWORK ACTIVITIES WITH
HIGHER EDUCATION

The aging network is integral to higher education. Students in almost every area of gerontology and geriatrics must be able to interact with older people and the systems and programs designed to provide assistance to them. We have identified three important ways that the aging network provides critical support to higher education: field placements, involvement with academic programs, and research opportunities.

FIELD PLACEMENTS/SERVICE
LEARNING/MENTORING

Important learning opportunities take place outside the walls of the classroom when students engage in field placements such as internships or service learning. Higher education programs that weave work experience or other practice-related exposure into the curriculum give students an edge. Time spent in the work world of a student's chosen field offers valuable career-testing, enhances resumes, and also opens the door to career-related mentoring. When these collaborative efforts between higher education and the aging network are at their best, learning opportunities open to faculty and workplace staff in addition to the participating students (Jarosz & Johnson-Bogart, 1996).

As was the case for the research relationship, we see a range of models used to define the parameters for these activities. In some instances the university approaches the practitioner agency and asks if it is willing to accept students. The university faculty, the student, and the agency essentially negotiate the terms of the work relationship, addressing such issues as intern and agency responsibilities, time frame, remuneration, products, expected outcomes, and liability. Agencies are typically pleased to have students involved with the organization, and by and large this model works reasonably well.

A second approach involves agencies that have decided that it is important to their organization to include interns in their ongoing management activities. These agencies often allocate stipends or other organizational resources to interns. They generally have a clear idea of the type of activities that they would like interns to be involved with, and often have developed a supervisory structure to ensure that the experience is a sound one for the student. These internships are driven more by the host agency need rather than the expressed need of the student.

A third model is a collaborative one between agency and university. Under this system the agency and the university enter into a dialogue where each entity, and hopefully the student as well, brings its needs and goals to the table prior to a particular student assignment. Both organizations can articulate what they think is most important to be achieved in the internship, and there is a shared understanding of how the experience can accomplish these goals. As was the case for the research collaboration, this approach requires that the university and the practice organization have, or develop, an ongoing relationship, and takes more up-front time for both groups. Our university is in the process of using this model with a local continuing care retirement community that is developing an alternative approach to nursing home service delivery. The retirement community felt like the traditional administrator-in-training (AIT) approach for nursing homes was just not appropriate for the small alternative homes. Together, all parties, including the student, were able to design a practicum that would work for the retirement community and the university.

In each of these models it is common for aging network professionals to be field instructors, or adjunct or clinical faculty members. In many gerontology or geriatric programs, such as medicine, social work, nursing, and administration, these faculty members are absolutely critical to the successful education of the student. Without these resources the type and quality of the education received by students would be incomplete.

INVOLVEMENT WITH ACADEMIC PROGRAMS

Professionals from the practice world have been an important resource for academic programs. In many instances, programs rely on professionals to serve on advisory committees to assist with overall design, curriculum development, internships, and job placement. Although there is limited discussion of these types of arrangements in the gerontological literature, numerous programs have discussed the use of advisory committees in the development and refinement of programs. Our master's program in gerontology used an advisory committee during the initial development stage and then returned to a reconfigured advisory group composed of network members and alumni to update and refine the program.

RESEARCH OPPORTUNITIES

Gaining access to research opportunities is critical for many students in gerontology. Although we have discussed potential models for linking faculty researchers and practitioner agencies, in this section we specifically address student access. Systematic data on the number and range of studies undertaken by students does not exist. However, at a recent statewide conference in Ohio more than 20 student presentations based on access to community data were presented. A wide array of student papers can be found at national meetings in gerontology as well. In light of the number of gerontology and geriatric programs across the United States, it appears that each year thousands of students conduct research studies in the field as part of their educational activities. This opportunity provides the essential first steps for student researchers and generates valuable information for the network.

JOINT PROGRAM DEVELOPMENT

A final category includes projects that are developed jointly between higher education and the aging network. This group includes the joint research and educational partnerships discussed earlier, plus a programmatic dimension. For example, a number of universities and continuing care retirement communities have partnered to develop a retirement community located on the college campus (Krout & Pogorzala, 2002; Moore, 2004). Such partnerships provide benefits to both entities as retirees find college campuses an attractive location to retire, and university alumni find the option attractive. Universities like the idea of being able to bring alums back to campus and hope that this model will provide current students with an opportunity to work with the retirement community. Universities also hope that such an arrangement could enhance alumni contributions.

A second example involves university and aging network providers who are able to develop a marketable intervention. The interest in evidence-based practice initiatives has created a market for proven interventions that can include a training and research component involving a practice/university partnership. A third example involves a partnership that developed a training center for workers in the field of aging. Although still relatively rare, these efforts represent the development of a new relationship between higher education and the aging network.

OVERVIEW OF AGING NETWORK/ HIGHER EDUCATION ACTIVITIES

To summarize this discussion we present in Table 9.1 an overview of the array of activities generated by each component of the higher education/aging network partnership. It might be instructive for both aging network and higher education organizations that deem this relationship as a priority to systematically review their current activities. For example, in viewing a formal degree program one can raise a series of questions about the interface between higher education and the aging network. Does the academic program use an advisory committee composed of network professionals to design or review its educational program? In turn, does the aging network provide student education opportunities, such as internships or service learning? Finally, to what extent is there a partnership in the educational mission? Are there efforts to develop joint continuing education programs?

In the community area, do faculty members serve on agency advisory boards or boards of directors? Do aging network professionals serve as field or clinical faculty? Is there a relationship between the university and key aging network providers? In looking at the research relationship do university researchers conduct studies in the applied aging network setting? Do aging network providers allocate resources for research activities? Are there efforts to jointly develop a research agenda that is mutually beneficial to higher education and the aging network? Finally, have higher education and the aging network been involved in program development? One of the more visible examples of this type of collaboration is the university-based or college-linked continuing care retirement community. Others may be more applied, such as the development of a training center for home care workers.

These examples and the dimensions that they cover are a starting point for an assessment of partnership activities. There are many additions that could be identified, depending on the circumstances of individual programs, disciplines, and geographic regions. These questions are designed as a place to start in viewing the current partnership activities and planning for future efforts.

TABLE 9.1

Aging Network/Higher Education Linkage Activities (a Self-Review)

Higher education	Aging network
Formal degree program	**Formal degree program**
1. Use of advisory committee to develop or modify program	1. Provide practicum experiences (including paid student internships)
2. Systematic data collection to assess program value to provider	2. Service learning opportunities
Continuing education	**Continuing education**
1. Developed in conjunction with provider network	1. Staff participate in continuing education
2. Offered in partnership with aging network providers	2. Provide input on continuing education program offerings and structure
3. Involved with Institute for Learning in Retirement	3. Offer joint programs
4. Offer consultation to network organizations	
Faculty involvement in network	**Aging network in higher education**
1. Faculty and staff serve on advisory boards or boards of directors	1. Serve on academic advisory committees
2. Faculty and staff serve as consultants to network providers	2. Serve as adjunct or clinical faculty
Research activities with aging network providers	**Research activities with higher education**
1. University staff involved in active research project with network	1. Research site for faculty and students
2. University staff involved in externally funded research effort	2. Provide resources to conduct research
3. Joint research project	3. Joint research project

Program development

1. Partnership to develop joint project such as a retirement community on university campus
2. Efforts to market results of evidence-based practice program
3. Development of training center

CONCLUSION

Both higher education and the aging network have been able to develop their niche in today's aging society. Gerontological education has expanded, and while it faces challenges in attracting students and research and training funds, it has grown dramatically and is arguably stronger than it was two decades ago. The aging network has grown to become a major component of the health, social service, and long-term care delivery system, despite facing ongoing resource limitations. If the current demographic boom were not on the horizon, it is possible that gerontological education and the aging network providers could continue to move forward under their current structure, where each provides limited support to the other, and autonomy and distance is the hallmark of the relationship.

However, the demographic reality is upon us, and this means that both entities face crucial challenges. Universities face resource constraints and pressures both for students and research dollars. Programs that have trouble attracting students, no matter how much they may benefit society, will struggle for resources. At the same time, it is clear that the service dollars available to the aging network can not grow proportionally with the size of the aging population. This means that the network will not be able to use the same approaches to serving tomorrow's older population. The development of an educated workforce and ensuring that programs are effective and efficient will require a new paradigm to educate and serve our aging society. The traditional approach, which involves both groups operating primarily independently, will not result in a significant enough change for either gerontological education or the aging network to respond to future challenges.

In order to meet these growing challenges, it is our contention that the gerontology and geriatric education programs and the aging network providers that will succeed in the future will be those organizations that move to the collaborative model. To be successful, both sets of organizations have to approach the collaboration as a partnership. Relationships need to be established, and both entities will need to recognize the differences and commonalities between higher education and the aging network. It is this change in perspective that will result in the type of innovation in both education and service delivery that will be necessary if both groups are to truly succeed in this aging society.

REFERENCES

The American Geriatrics Society. (2008). *Loan forgiveness*. Retrieved March 29, 2008, from http://www.americangeriatrics.org/policy/loan-forgiveness.shtml

Anderson, T. B. (1999). Aging education in higher education: Preparing for the 21st century. *Educational Gerontology, 25*(6), 571–579.

Applebaum, R., Kunkel, S., & Wilson, K. (2007). Transforming data into practical information: Using consumer input to improve home-care services. *The Gerontologist, 47*(1), 116–122.

Blanchette, P. L., & Flynn, B. (2001). Geriatric medicine: An approaching crisis. *Generations, 25*(1), 80–84.

Braun, K. L., Cheang, M., & Shigeta, D. (2005). Increasing knowledge, skills, and empathy among direct care workers in elder care: A preliminary study of an active-learning model. *The Gerontologist, 45*(1), 118–124.

Cummings, S. M., & Adler, G. (2007). Predictors of social workers employment in gerontological work. *Educational Gerontology, 33*(11), 925–938.

Cyert, R. M., & Goodman, P. S. (1997). Creating effective university-industry alliances: An organizational learning perspective. *Organizational Dynamics, 25*(4), 45–57.

Deadrick, D. L., & Gibson, P. A. (2007). An examination of the research-practice gap in HR: Comparing topics of interest to HR academics and HR professionals. *Human Resource Management Review, 17*(2), 131–139.

Dorothy I. Height and Whitney M. Young, Jr. Social Work Reinvestment Act, H.R. 5447, 110th Congress, 2nd Session, (2008).

Guest, D. E. (2007). Don't shoot the messenger: A wake-up call for academics. *Academy of Management Journal, 50*(5), 1020–1026.

Haley, W. E., & Zelinski, E. (2007). Progress and challenges in graduate education in gerontology: The U.S. experience. *Gerontology and Geriatrics Education, 27*(2), 11–26.

Jarosz, L., & Johnson-Bogart, K., (1996). New concepts of the relationship between college and community. *College Teaching, 44*(3), 83–88.

Krout, J. A., & Pogorzala, C. H. (2002). An intergenerational partnership between a college and congregate housing facility. *The Gerontologist, 42*(6), 853–858.

Langer, N. (1999). Gerontolizing health care: A train-the-trainer program for nurses. *Gerontology and Geriatrics Education, 19*(4), 47–56.

Levin, S. A., Brett, B., Robinson, B. E., Stratos, G. A., Lascher, S. M., Granville, L., et al. (2007). Practicing physician education in geriatrics: Lessons learned from a train-the-trainer model. *Journal of the American Geriatrics Society, 55*(8), 1281–1286.

Lubben, J., & Harooytan, L. K. (2002). Strengthening geriatric social work through a doctoral fellowship program. *Journal of Gerontological Social Work, 39*(1/2), 145–156.

Moore, M. T. (2004, May 20) Grads return to campuses to stay: Universities lure devoted alumni to live in golf-course communities. *USA Today,* p. A03.

Murdoch, L., Kunkel, S., Applebaum, R., & Straker, J. (2004). Care managers as research interviewers: A test of a strategy for gathering consumer satisfaction. *Journal of Applied Gerontology, 23*(3), 234–246.

Peterson, D. A., Douglass, E. B., & Whittington, J. L. (2004). *Careers in aging: opportunities and options*. Association for Gerontology in Higher Education. Washington, DC.

Robertson, J. F., & Cummings, C. C. (1996). Attracting nurses to long-term care. *Journal of Gerontological Nursing, 22*(9), 24–32.

Rynes, S. L., Giluk, T. L., & Brown, K. G. (2007). The very separate worlds of academic and practitioner periodicals in human resource management: Implications for evidence-based management. *The Academy of Management Journal, 50*(5), 987–1008.

Sabir, M., Breckman, R., Meador, R., Wethington, E., Reid, M. C., & Pillemer, K. (2006). The CITRA research-practice consensus-workshop model: Exploring a new method of research translation in aging. *The Gerontologist, 46*(6), 833–839.

Waites, C., & Bearon, L. (2007). Cross-professional partnerships: Innovation in continuing education for social workers and extension educators. *Educational Gerontology, 33*(10), 833–853.

CHAPTER 10

A Philosophical Foundation for Multimedia Design in Gerontology and Geriatrics

Donna M. Weinreich and Jennifer Mendez

Multimedia teaching and learning approaches in gerontology and geriatrics were examined through an extensive literature review and Internet search, and comparison with guidelines developed by the Association for Gerontology in Higher Education. Systematic research investigating scientific foundations for multimedia design in gerontology and geriatrics technology-based or technology-enhanced teaching strategies were not found. The seven principles of good practice, the psychological principles of learner-centered teaching, and Mayer's principles of multimedia design are described as a point of convergence among learner, instructor, and learning environment. This point of convergence is suggested as a starting point for research in the efficacy of multimedia design in gerontology and geriatrics.

Keywords: gerontology; geriatrics; learner-centered; student-centered; multimedia learning; principles of multimedia learning

Institutions of higher education have been investing in nontraditional methods of instructional delivery for quite some time (Weinreich & Tompkins, 2006), so much so that they are now considered ordinary rather than innovative. Since the 1990s a variety of technologies have been used for instructional delivery; for example, Internet-based asynchronous courseware and interactive two-way synchronous modalities, which outweigh other technologies

DOI: 10.1891/0198-8794.28.149

such as one-way audio/video combinations and CD-ROM (Tompkins & Weinreich, 2007). Teaching with technology encompasses courseware, like WebCT and Black Board Vista; virtual elements, such as virtual clients (Weinreich & Tompkins, 2006); and environments, like virtual surgical suites.

As institutions continue to adopt technological applications as teaching tools we have found a lack of systematic investigation of the underlying psychology and philosophy of good course design in high-tech environments.

MULTIMEDIA LEARNING

Since institutions of higher education have embraced the use of technology in various ways it has become known as multimedia learning. However, no evidence was found of a systematic examination of the psychological and philosophical foundations of multimedia learning in general and in gerontology and geriatrics education specifically. Indeed, content areas that have generated the most research in multimedia learning are: reading, mathematics, chemistry, meteorology, complex physical systems, language, and cognitive skills (Mayer, 2005, p. 7). Research has also been conducted in advanced computer-based content areas: animated pedagogical agents, virtual reality, games, simulations, microworlds, hypermedia, and e-courses.

There is no reason for gerontology and geriatrics not to be among the content areas being examined. Published research in gerontology and geriatrics has concerned student satisfaction and learner-centered instruction (Weinreich, in press), the use of virtual patients in medical education (e.g. Orton & Mulhausen, 2008), eLearning tutorials (e.g., Ruiz, Smith, Rodriguez, Zuilen, & Mintzer, 2007), and consumer-related interfaces (e.g., Tarlow & Mahoney, 2007). While this is very important work, examining a scientific foundation for the actual construction of technology-based or technology-enhanced gerontological instruction seems critical. This chapter discusses a philosophical foundation where three specific areas converge: the seven principles of good practice (Chickering & Ehrmann, 1996), the psychological principles of learner-centered teaching (American Psychological Association, 2008), and multimedia design (Mayer, 2005).

The Seven Principles of Good Practice

Chickering and Ehrmann (1996) discussed technology in relation to the seven principles of good practice. Although developed nearly 20 years ago, these principles are just as relevant today. The principles outline the learning obligations between instructor and student. If the principles are embraced,

TABLE 10.1

Instructor/Student Obligations Associated With the Seven Principles of Good Practice

Instructor's obligations	Students' obligations
Substantive contact with students Prompt feedback	Reciprocity and collaboration among their peers
Good time management	Active learning
Communication of high expectations	Good time management
Respect for diverse talents and ways of learning	Respect for diverse talents and ways of learning

technology can augment the learning experience. The principles are shown in Table 10.1.

The Psychological Principles of Learner-Centered Teaching

The American Psychological Association (APA) has developed psychological principles for learner-centered teaching (APA, 2008). While these principles were developed for traditional didactic classroom situations, they are also helpful when considering technologically enhanced instruction. For example, these components were discussed by McCombs and Vakili (2005) in conjunction with a learner-centered eLearning framework. The principles are mapped in a four-factor model: (a) cognitive, (b) motivational, (c) developmental, and (d) individual differences.

Attending to these factors and their underlying principles takes into account the individual learner and articulates the significance of unique learner characteristics in the academic environment. For detailed discussions see McCombs and Vakili (2005) and the APA's Center for Psychology in Schools and Education.

The APA psychological principles can be observed in Mayer's principles of multimedia design in other content areas previously noted. Research in Mayer's principles has shown the impact of the psychological principles on individual learners.

Mayer's Principles of Multimedia Design

Mayer's (2005) principles concern the practical foundations on which technology-based educational delivery systems are constructed. They are divided into two categories, basic and advanced. Table 10.2 shows how these principles are organized. While all of the principles should be of concern to educators in gerontology and geriatrics, those of particular note are split-attention,

TABLE 10.2

Mayer's Principles of Multimedia Design

Basic principles	Advanced principles
Multimedia	Guided discovery
Split-attention	Worked-out example
Modality	Collaboration
Redundancy	Self-explanation
Segmenting	Animation and interactivity
Coherence, signaling, spatial	Navigation
contiguity, and temporal contiguity	Site map
Personalization	Prior knowledge
	Cognitive aging

segmenting, guided discovery, self-explanation, and prior knowledge. Simply put, *split-attention* takes into consideration multiple channels for learning (e.g., auditory and visual processing). *Segmenting* of presentation materials provides clear organization and reduced redundancy. *Guided discovery* allows learners to investigate the veracity of their own propositions. *Self-explanation* occurs when the learner articulates her understanding of the content based on experience. And *prior knowledge* is what a learner brings (or doesn't bring) to the learning experience. These principles are examined in more detail in the "Discussion" section of this chapter.

These three sets of principles are offered here as a philosophical foundation for the use of technology as an instructional strategy for gerontology and geriatrics.

METHODS

An extensive literature review was conducted using these databases: EBSCOhost; ERIC; PsycINFO; Social Work Abstracts; Medline; Firstsearch; Wilson-SelectPlus; WestCat; and WorldCat.

We found specific journals focused on the use of technology and teaching. The last 10 years of these journals were searched. They included: *Gerontology and Geriatrics Education, Computers in Healthcare* (later replaced by *Technology in Healthcare*), *Journal of Teaching in Social Work,* and *Health Informatics Journal.*

Ultimately, 500 peer-reviewed journal articles were reviewed. These articles concerned student satisfaction, learner-centered instruction (Weinreich, in press), and the use of computers by older adults. As noted earlier, other facets of this literature described virtual patients, eLearning tutorials, and consumer-related interfaces. Based on this literature review, two considerations were examined:

a. The Association for Gerontology in Higher Education (AGHE) standards for teaching with technology
b. The types of technology being used to teach gerontology and geriatrics and how

Consideration 1

We examined the AGHE standards for teaching with technology, which provided curriculum and faculty guidelines for degree and certificate programs that could be applied to online programs. It offered basic considerations and discussed administrative and policy issues involved in offering an Internet-based program. Three main types of online programs addressed student needs, programs that:

1. Provide matriculated students with either full or partial online courses,
2. Offer online courses to students who have not matriculated in the academic institution, and
3. Reach out to international students residing in other countries (to be treated as [2]). (Lucchino, Parham, & Lane, 2005)

The standards also addressed administrative issues such as the institution's ability to offer online courses, faculty preparedness, conducting evaluations and assessments, as well as portals for online course resources. However, there was no unique gerontology curriculum content or faculty qualifications offered that would be exclusive to online or Internet-based teaching. The regular classroom *AGHE Standards and Guidelines for Gerontology Programs* (2005) were recommended.

These standards are not in-depth guidelines or a resource on the subject matter of geriatrics and gerontology but provide generic mechanisms for developing an online course. There is no reference to theory, practice, or other aging service considerations that an instructor or faculty members could use to develop or teach a gerontology or geriatrics course online.

Bucur (2000) assists gerontologists and geriatricians to understand how to design, create, and deploy online courses using currently available Internet tools and concepts. In other resources like *The Cambridge Handbook of Age and Ageing* (Johnson, 2005) discussion of Internet-based or Internet-accessed materials are rare.

Consideration 2

To determine the types of technology currently in use to teach gerontology and geriatrics, the authors conducted a systematic review of public, online curricula using these search terms: eLearning, eTeaching, gerontology geriatrics, Stanford Geriatric Education, and Portal of Geriatric Online Educations (POGOe). While not an exhaustive list, these representative Internet sites were captured:

> AARP's *Age Source Worldwide* (AARP, 2008) offers databases, libraries, directories, statistical resources, bibliographies, and reading lists, and so forth focused on aging.
>
> The American Geriatrics Society (2008) assists students, residents, and practicing physicians in determining or advancing their career goals by providing practice guidelines to improve the health, independence, and quality of life of older persons.
>
> Geriatric Web (University of South Carolina, 2008) is a geriatrics digital library used in the education of health care professionals and in the clinical care of older patients. It offers geriatric syndrome and organ-specific information.
>
> GeriaSims (University of Iowa, 2008) are interactive online learning programs for health care professionals and trainees. It includes patient care simulations on issues often encountered in the care of elderly patients. In each simulation, users ask history questions, perform virtual physical exams, order tests, consult with specialists and other health care professionals, and make decisions about diagnosis, treatment, and other care issues. Feedback is provided regarding decisions and users may ask questions of a simulated mentor to access didactic information about the topic of the simulation.
>
> GERI Pearls (University of Nebraska Medical Center, 2008) are downloadable pocket cards that are short, concise reviews of geriatric topics like aging pharmacology, constipation, delirium, dementia, depression, falls, insomnia, hospital admission, pain management, palliative care, preoperative assessment, pressure ulcers, syncope, urinary incontinence, and weight loss.
>
> POGOe (Portal of Geriatric Education Online, 2008) is an online clearinghouse for dissemination of geriatric educational products. It offers medical educators materials that may be integrated into the

geriatric content of their courses. This site also offers links to more focused course content like the July 2007 AAMC and John A. Hartford Foundation Consensus Conference on Competencies; the Spring 2008 AAMC Medical School Graduate Revised Geriatrics-Related Questionnaire (GQ); the Donald Reynolds Education Products Inventory; and the Online Hartford Resource Center. Faculty teaching geriatrics are able to use peer-reviewed products like virtual patients and problem-based case studies intended to allow learners to get a better understanding of the complex issues involved in treating a geriatric patient.

WebMD (2008) is an encyclopedic educational resource used by professionals as well as older adults and their families.

The sites listed here just scratch the surface of information available to teachers of geriatrics and gerontology in the development of course materials. Many provide not only case examples but also quizzes to test competencies and knowledge. However, discussion of the underlying principles of their design was not found.

DISCUSSION

It is quite surprising to find no discussion of systematic approaches to content design in virtual learning environments. A serious examination is warranted where Mayer's principles, Chickering and Ehrmann's (1996) seven principles of good practice, and the learner-centered psychological principles converge.

MAYER'S PRINCIPLES

Mayer emphasizes the learner-centered approach in multimedia design. This is grounded in our understanding of how the mind works and how multimedia can enhance an individual's learning (Mayer, 2005). The focus of this chapter will not permit discussion of all of the principles. However, what the authors believe to be the most cogent principles for gerontology and geriatrics education at this time are discussed.

Basic Principle: The Split-Attention Principle

Research has shown that the brain possesses discrete processing channels for the senses. While learning is not limited to auditory and visual processing, they are the most researched modalities of learning. What has been learned is that providing simultaneous input to multiple channels enhances learning, while providing sequential input hampers learning (Ayres & Sweller, 2005).

Basic Principle: The Segmenting Principle

When using technology to teach, chunking information emulates the familiar action of turning pages in a book. This paces the delivery of information in more manageable pieces (chunks) and assists the learner in several ways, allowing for: better time management, reduced pressure, and increased organization. This could be extrapolated to future older clients who could benefit because the learner engaged the material as deeply as possible. Segmenting encourages a clearer organization of presentation materials and opportunities to reduce redundancy.

Advanced Principle: The Guided Discovery Principle

Guided discovery utilizes the induction method of scientific inquiry. The learner (with the assistance of the instructor) develops testable hypotheses based on current knowledge and experience (de Jong, 2005). Knowledge is acquired as empirical observations support or refute the hypotheses. Learners take on the role of the scientist and investigate the veracity of the propositions that interest them within a specified context and content area.

Advanced Principle: The Self-Explanation Principle

An integral part of the learning process is developing the capacity to generate explanations of the things observed. The learner is required to integrate information from a variety of venues (Roy & Chi, 2005). Learners engage material in different, meaningful ways and monitor and articulate their own evolving understanding of the content based on their experiences.

Advanced Principle: The Prior Knowledge Principle

The level of a learner's prior knowledge figures prominently in how *well* he or she learns what the instructor believes to be new material. As learners advance through a course or a curriculum, too much review of old material can actually hamper the ability to learn and integrate new material. Conscious consideration of what a learner brings (or doesn't bring) to the learning experience is essential.

CONCLUSION

The reader may have noticed in this brief overview of Mayer's principles the emergence of the seven principles of good practice and the psychological principles of learner-centered teaching. The relationship between learner and instructor and the learner's psychological readiness are key features of the successful application of Mayer's principles.

Cognitive load theory suggests that the human brain possesses separate channels for processing sensory information and that finite amounts of memory resources are dedicated to each channel. While learning is not restricted to the visual and auditory channels, these channels have received the most attention. Reducing cognitive load improves learning by facilitating long-term retention and integration.

Two ways to help reduce cognitive load are:

1. Contiguity—coordinating verbal and visual information
2. Coherence—managing extraneous information (Fletcher & Tobias, 2005).

Depending on how verbal and visual information are coordinated, the greatest improvements have been observed in transfer—applying what has been learned. Manipulation of knowledge from long-term memory is required to perform tasks such as taking a blood pressure reading or acquiring an accurate history from an older client. Presenting verbal and visual information simultaneously rather than successively seems to reduce cognitive load, making it less taxing to sift, organize, and file what is being presented.

Conscious decisions should be made about what is most important to communicate. Research shows that learners retain and apply more from a well-written chapter synopsis than from the complete chapter. This suggests that educators should concentrate on presenting the core idea and eliminate extraneous or irrelevant material (no matter how interesting). For example, it has been shown that a diagram of the action of the heart is sufficient for college level learners. The concept of prior knowledge suggests that a verbal (or text) description is extraneous.

Such compactness also provides opportunities for self explanation. Learners should be given multiple, appropriately timed opportunities to develop personal meaning-making. More than in any other fields, students of gerontology and geriatrics are bombarded with complex, multifaceted content. They are then asked to apply it in complex, often time-sensitive, situations. Providing opportunities for self-explanation—integrating content earlier than traditional educational opportunities provide—could create deeper, more complete learning.

This can be accommodated by giving the learner as much control of the multimedia environment as possible. For example, presentation components can be layered in such a manner that learners can turn them on and off.

Progressive reductions in detail could accomplish the same goal of simplifying the learning environment.

Kalyuga (2005) reviewed the research on prior knowledge. He found redundancy was a frequent method of reinforcement. However, while redundancy was effective for novice learners, it was an impediment for advanced learners. This is called the *expertise reversal effect* (Kalyuga, Ayeres, Chandler, & Sweller, 2003). In order to accommodate changing dominant cognitive activities, strategies like scaffolding (gradually replacing highly structured designs with less structured designs) and segmenting could be used.

Equally important is splitting the learner's attention (Ayres & Sweller, 2005). Research has shown that forcing learners to mentally integrate multiple sources of information is deleterious to learning because it causes unwarranted cognitive load.

Much of the current education literature in gerontology and geriatrics has concerned comparisons of student satisfaction with the teaching modality (e.g., eLearning vs. lecture). Because research is needed on the construction of the educational presentation, particular consideration must be given to the intersection among:

- The compact between learner and instructor that establishes the individuals' obligations in a successful learning endeavor,
- The psychological readiness of a learner to engage gerontology and geriatric content on a deep and meaningful level,
- The coordination of course goals aimed at teaching theory as well as clinical skills,
- The management of the learning environment such that acquired knowledge can be transferred to practice with older persons,
- The learner's status as novice or expert (or somewhere in between), as this impacts cognitive load and the learner's capacity to transfer knowledge to the clinical setting,
- The learner's level of interest in the subject matter, taking into account the vulnerability of the older population,
- The gerontologist or geriatrician as instructor, taking into account leadership and presentation styles and their expectations of learners,
- The cognitive load that might interfere with the development of critical clinical skills that might put an older person at extreme risk of harm,
- The expected outcomes that include better geriatric care and heightened sensitivity to the needs of the older client, and
- The learner-specific psychological and physical aspects of learning.

TABLE 10.3

Mayer's Principles in Relation to Gerontology and Geriatrics Education

	Mayer's principles	Weinreich/Mendez application principles
	Basic principles	**Gerontology/geriatrics**
Multimedia	Are words and pictures presented together?	Are the relevant components of the presentation offered simultaneously?
Split-attention	Are words and pictures physically integrated?	Has the visual presentation been organized to prevent the learner from having to manage multiple sources of information at once?
Modality	Are graphics augmented by narration instead of text?	Is the use of the brain's multiple channels maximized, while minimizing overload on any single channel?
Redundancy	Is information presented in only one format?	Is repetition eliminated?
Segmenting	Are learner-paced segments used rather than a continuous unit?	Is material chunked in logical ways?
Coherence, signaling, spatial contiguity, and temporal contiguity	Is extraneous material excluded? Are cues present that highlight the organization of essential material? Are pictures and words presented near each other?	Does the presentation consist of essential core knowledge, minimizing cognitive overload?
	Advanced principles	
Personalization	Are words presented in a conversational rather than a formal style?	Is the traditional lecture format welcoming to the learner?
		Collaborative Principles
Guided discovery	Is guidance incorporated into a discovery-based environment?	Are opportunities created for student–older adult interaction (e.g., intergenerational biographies)?
Worked-out example	Is a worked-out example provided when initial skills are being taught?	Are specific examples of communicating with older adults provided?

(continued)

TABLE 10.3 (continued)

	Advanced principles	Collaborative Principles
Collaboration	Are collaborative online learning activities incorporated?	Are online activities developed with community partners that explore clinical settings?
Self-explanation	Are learners encouraged to generate self-explanations during learning?	Are students encouraged to express the meaning they make from guided discovery activities with seniors?
Animation and interactivity	Are animation or static diagrams present?	Are animated demonstrations designed to specifically enhance the learner's capacity to address the needs of older adults?
Navigation	Are appropriate navigation aids present in hypertext environments?	Do case studies encourage and enable learners to visit other Web pages (e.g., elder abuse sites, sexual violence and older adults)?
Site map	Is there a map showing where the learner is in an online environment?	Is the online environment organized in such a way that the learner's stress/anxiety is minimized and engagement in gerontology/geriatric content is maximized?
Prior knowledge	Is the content appropriate for novice learners or expert learners?	Have basic concept and theories of aging (e.g., Neugarten's [1973] young-old and old-old) been incorporated in novel ways to encourage the novice learner to discuss them and for the advanced learner to integrate/reinforce them?
Cognitive aging	Does the instructional design expand working memory capacity for older learners?	Has the instructional design taken into account older, nontraditional learners by addressing cognitive load by utilizing Echt, Morrell, and Park's (1998) concepts for older learners and computers?

These critical features of instruction must be examined systematically if we are to facilitate our learners effectively in an increasingly complex world, particularly when they will be working with our oldest and most vulnerable clients.

Examining our construction of course materials—whether single or multimedia—by considering the seven principles of good practice, the psychological principles of learner-centered teaching, and Mayer's principles, will enhance our capacity to lead well and enable our learners to learn effectively.

We suggest that educators integrate these principles in such a way as to enhance education in gerontology and geriatrics by mindfully examining how educational strategies are constructed. Mayer's principles are listed in Table 10.3, accompanied by the basic question each principle is trying to address (column 2). Added to these principles are the Weinreich/Mendez application principles for gerontology and geriatrics (column 3). These application principles are intended to initiate the discussion of an organized examination of the construction of technology-based or technology-enhanced instruction in gerontology and geriatrics. Basic application principles address maximizing the learning environment while simplifying what the learner is required to cognitively process. Advanced principles address connecting the learner with a very specific client population—older adults—by providing guidance and opportunities for self-explanation and active discovery.

The reader will notice that the basic principles for gerontology and geriatrics closely mirror Mayer's principles. This is largely due to the fact that they are the fundamental building blocks of successful multimedia design. They capture the instructor's obligations of the seven principles of good practice and take into consideration the psychological principles of learner-centered teaching. Mayer's basic principles are the foundation of the visual and auditory contribution of teaching with multimedia.

Once the stage is set using the basic principles, advanced principles address learner-centered teaching in a holistic manner. They again take into account the seven principles of good practice and the psychological principles of learner-centered teaching; however, this is done in more complex ways by allowing for the learner's unique cognitive and emotional ways of processing material. There is a need in gerontology and geriatrics education to systematically explore all of these principles and develop a scientific foundation for the application of multimedia design.

REFERENCES

AARP. (2008). *AgeSource worldwide.* Retrieved February 5, 2008, from http://www. aarp.org/research/agesource/

American Geriatrics Society. (2008). *AGS training and curriculum guidelines*. Retrieved February 5, 2008, from http://www.americangeriatrics.org/education/

American Psychological Association. (2006). *Coalition for psychology in schools and education*. Retrieved September 1, 2008, from http://www.apa.org/ed/cpse/lcpp_taskforce.html

American Psychological Association. (1997). *Learner-centered psychological principles: A framework for school reform and redesign*. Retrieved September 1, 2008, from http://www.apa.org/ed/cpse/LCPP.pdf

Association for Gerontology in Higher Education. (2005). *Standards and guidelines for gerontology programs* (4th ed.). Washington D.C.: AGHE Standards Committee.

Ayres, P., & Sweller, J. (2005). The split-attention principle in multimedia learning. In R. Mayer (Ed.), *The Cambridge handbook of multimedia learning* (pp. 135–146). Cambridge, MA: Cambridge University Press.

Bucur, A. (2000). Components of online education in gerontology. *Journal of Gerontology and Geriatrics Education, 20*(4), 31–46.

Chickering, A. W., & Ehrmann, S. C. (1996). *Implementing the seven principles: Technology as lever*. Retrieved August 19, 2005, from http://www.tltgroup.org/programs/seven/html

de Jong, T. (2005). The guided discovery principle in multimedia learning. In R. Mayer (Ed.), *The Cambridge handbook of multimedia learning* (pp. 215–228). Cambridge, MA: Cambridge University Press.

Echt, K., Morrell, R., & Park, D. (1998). Effects of age and training formats on basic computer skill acquisition in older adults. *Educational Gerontology, 24*(1), 3–25.

Fletcher, J., & Tobias, S. (2005). The multimedia principle. In R. Mayer (Ed.), *The Cambridge handbook of multimedia learning* (pp. 117–133). Cambridge, MA: Cambridge University Press.

Johnson, M. L. (2005). *The Cambridge handbook of age and ageing* (Bengtson, Coleman, and Kirkwood, Eds.). Cambridge, UK: Cambridge University Press.

Kalyuga, S. (2005). Prior knowledge principle in multimedia learning. In R. Mayer (Ed.), *The Cambridge handbook of multimedia learning* (pp. 325–337). Cambridge, MA: Cambridge University Press.

Kalyuga, S., Ayeres, P., Chandler, P., & Sweller, J. (2003). Expertise reversal effect. *Educational Psychologist, 38*, 23–31.

Lucchino, R., Parham, I., & Lane, W. (2005). On-line courses/programs in gerontology. In Gugliucci, Moore, & Miller (Eds.), *Association for Gerontology in Higher Education standards and guidelines for gerontology programs* (4th ed., pp. 62–66). Washington, DC: AGHE.

Mayer, R. (Ed.). (2005). *The Cambridge handbook of multimedia design*. Cambridge, MA: Cambridge University Press.

Mayer, R. (2005). Principles for managing essential processing in multimedia learning: Segment, pretraining, and modality principles. In R. Mayer (Ed.), *The Cambridge handbook of multimedia learning* (pp. 169–182). Cambridge, MA: Cambridge University Press.

McCombs, B., & Vakili, D. (2005). A learner-centered framework for e-learning. *Teachers College Record, 107*(8), 1582–1600.

Neugarten, B. (1974). Age groups in American society and the rise of the young-old. *Annals of the American Academy of Political and Social Science, 415,* 187–198.

Orton, E., & Mulhausen, P. (2008). E-learning virtual patients for geriatric education. *Gerontology and Geriatrics Education, 28*(3), 73–88.

Portal of Geriatric Online Education. (2008). *What is POGOe?* Retrieved February 5, 2008, from http://www.pogoe.org/frames.aspx

Roy, M., & Chi, M. (2005). The self-explanation principle in multimedia learning. In R. Mayer (Ed.), *The Cambridge handbook of multimedia learning* (pp. 271–286). Cambridge, MA: Cambridge University Press.

Ruiz, J., Smith, M., Rodriguez, O., Zuilen, M., & Mintzer, M. (2007). An interactive e-learning tutorial for medical students on how to conduct the performance-oriented mobility assessment. *Gerontology and Geriatrics Education, 27*(1), 51–60.

Tompkins, C., & Weinreich, D. M. (2007). Collaborating, teaching and learning in cyberspace: A virtual AGE experience. *Journal of Gerontological Social Work, 50*(1/2), 119–134.

Tralow, B., & Mahoney, D. (2005). Parity in computer-based health education: Designing culturally relevant Alzheimer's disease information. *Health Informatics Journal, 1*(3), 211–224.

University of Iowa. (2008). *GeriaSims.* Retrieved February 5, 2008, from http://www.healthcare.uiowa.edu/igec/e-learn_lic/geriasims/default.asp

University of Nebraska Medical Center. (2008). *GERI Pearls.* Retrieved February 5, 2008, from http://app1.unmc.edu/intmed/geriatrics/index.cfm?webtype=graphics&CONREF=44

University of South Carolina. (2008). *Geriatric Web.* Retrieved February 5, 2008, from http://geriatricweb.sc.edu

WebMD. (2008). Retrieved March 2, 2008, from http://www.webmd.com/

Weinreich, D. M. The path to learner-centered teaching. *Gerontology and Geriatrics Education, 29*(3), 210–224.

Weinreich, D. M., & Tompkins, C. (2006). Learning objects and gerontology. *Educational Gerontology: an International Journal, 32*(2), 785–799.

CHAPTER 11

Education and Training of Community Health Professionals and Service Providers

Judith L. Howe

BACKGROUND

The aging of the United States population and the resulting imperative for training in geriatrics has been well documented (American Geriatrics Society Core Writing Group of the Task Force on the Future of Geriatric Medicine, 2005). The population 65 and over will increase from 35 million in 2000 to 40 million in 2010 (a 15% increase) and then to 55 million in 2020 (a 36% increase for that decade). Furthermore, the so-called oldest old, those 85 and over, are the most rapidly increasing age group, projected to increase from 4.2 million in 2000 to 6.1 million in 2010 (a 40% increase) and then to 7.3 million in 2020 (a 44% increase for that decade; AARP, 2005).

These older Americans have more than twice as many contacts with physicians than do younger persons, and they account for almost half of all days of hospital care (Lawhorne, 2005). In 2005, for example, over 13.2 million persons aged 65 and older were discharged from short stay hospitals. This is a rate of 3,596 for every 10,000 persons aged 65 and older, which is over three times the comparable rate for persons of all ages (Which

The author is grateful for the editorial and research assistance of Suzanne Goldhirsch, MSEd, MS.

DOI: 10.1891/0198-8794.28.165

was 1,174 per 10,000). The average length of stay for persons aged 65 and over was 5.5 days; the comparable rate for persons of all ages was 4.8 days. Older persons also averaged more office visits with doctors in 2005: 6.5 office visits for those aged 65–74 and 7.7 office visits for persons over 75, while persons aged 45–65 averaged only 3.9 office visits during that year (Department of Health and Human Services, 2007a). This disproportionate share of health care utilization is forecast to accelerate dramatically as the elderly segment of the population increases (Department of Health and Human Services, 2007a).

As the nation has become "grayer," there has also been a corresponding trend to longer life spans and a change in the nature of illness. Americans are not dying typically from acute diseases as they did in previous generations. Now, chronic diseases such as diabetes and heart disease are the major cause of illness, disability, and death in this country. In addition to the special needs associated with chronic illness, older persons in general have unique characteristics that differentiate them from younger populations. Thus, special training is needed to most effectively evaluate and treat frail, older persons. All too often, illnesses in older people are misdiagnosed, overlooked, or dismissed as the normal process of aging, simply because health care professionals are not trained to recognize how diseases and drugs affect older patients differently than younger patients.

Despite the demonstrated value of this specialized type of care for older patients, however, there are not enough health care professionals with the required geriatric training. As the population of older patients has been rapidly expanding, the number of certified geriatricians in the United States was shrinking by a third between 1998 and 2004. And this number is expected to decline substantially as the present initial cadre of geriatricians retires just as the baby boom generation becomes eligible for Medicare (Warshaw & Bragg, 2003). According to the report *Caring for Older Americans: The Future of Geriatric Medicine,* there will be only 1 geriatrician for every 7,665 older adults in 2030 (American Geriatrics Society, 2005). This disturbing paucity of geriatric physician specialists affects other health care disciplines as well. Less than 1% of nurses are certified in geriatrics, and only 3% of advanced practice nurses specialize in care of the older adult. Less than one-third of 1% of physical therapists are certified in geriatrics, and of the more than 200,000 pharmacists, only 720 have a geriatric certification. Social workers have no national certification for geriatric social work, and registered dieticians and dietetic technicians have no formal program in geriatric nutrition (White House Conference on Aging, 2005).

The well-publicized and looming shortage of health care providers with a specialization in geriatrics has galvanized a collaborative effort among health policy experts, advocates for seniors, academic health centers, government agencies, and private foundations to increase recruitment in the field of geriatrics, argue for better reimbursement and incentives, and work with medical schools and residency programs to integrate geriatric topics into the training programs of relevant medical subspecialties. However, despite these laudable efforts, the number of physicians and other health providers who are trained in geriatrics is lagging significantly compared to the growing older population. Thus, in light of the reality that there will never be enough geriatricians or geriatric specialists in nursing, social work, and other allied health professions, increased attention has been focused on enhancing the geriatric knowledge of health care professionals who provide frontline care for the elderly in the community (Americans for Nursing Shortage Relief, 2007; Resnick, 2007).

This chapter presents an overview of the current state of geriatric training and education programs for community health professionals and service providers. Topics include the rationale and goals of this training, the targeted disciplines, the benefits of training, a survey of curriculum domains, and a description of training methods and settings. In addition, this chapter will briefly explore sustainability issues and review several recommendations for future directions in this important effort to disseminate the principles of geriatrics to community-based health care professionals.

For the purposes of this discussion, a *health professional* is defined as an "individual who has received a certificate, an associate degree, a bachelor's degree, a master's degree, a doctoral degree, or post-baccalaureate training in a field relating to health care, and who shares in the responsibility for the delivery of health care services or related services" (Department of Health and Human Services, 2007a, p. 42). A *health care provider* is an organization or person who delivers health care in a systematic way professionally to any individual in need of these services. Community health workers (CHWs) are trained paraprofessionals who serve as health and human service resource persons in the communities where they live and work. Their roles include helping families access community-based resources, providing culturally appropriate education and outreach, and the delivering other nonclinical services, such as social support and advocacy. The focus of this chapter is the training of community health professionals and community service providers, and these terms will be used interchangeably. CHWs are not directly involved in the provision of clinical health services, and therefore although they have a very important role in the care of the nation's elderly, their training will not be discussed in this chapter.

RATIONALE AND GOALS OF TRAINING COMMUNITY HEALTH PROFESSIONALS IN GERIATRICS

The most important rationale for training community health professionals in geriatrics is to improve the quality of comprehensive care available to elders living in the community. In addition to better management of chronic conditions and acute illnesses, older persons experience an enhanced quality of life when they are connected to the health care system. They become aware of an array of community resources, including social, financial, educational, and housing services, and they are better able to obtain the tools needed for successful aging. Specifically, having access to a community-based provider decreases the incidence of adverse events such as emergency room visits, nursing home placement, and social isolation.

In addition to improving patient care, geriatric training for health professionals in the community has other benefits, including the following.

Developing Future Practitioners

In the national debate over how to successfully meet the health care challenges facing our aging society, one response that has gained significant attention is to identify the right set of community-based health professionals and paraprofessionals to work with the older adult population, and then to provide the education and training necessary for these people (White House Conference on Aging, 2005).

While training needs vary across disciplines and settings, well-designed and comprehensive programs will incorporate the following core principles of quality geriatric care: interdisciplinary teamwork, geriatric assessment, culturally competent practice, understanding rural and underserved populations, geriatric mental health, and planning for continuity across sites of care. Additional special training topics should include: palliative and end-of-life care, ethical and legal issues, elder mistreatment, oral health, hazards of hospitalization, polypharmacy, housing, and emergency preparedness (see Tables 11.1 and 11.2).

Advancing the Train-the-Trainer Model

In 2005, the Mini-Conference on Geriatric Health Care Workforce Issues of the White House Conference on Aging recommended a national policy to "educate and train all health care professionals, health professions students,

TABLE 11.1

Core Curricular Competencies

Core competency	Definition	Rationale
Interdisciplinary teamwork	An interdisciplinary health care team brings together a group of individuals with diverse training and education to work on an identified task. Teams can include physicians, social workers, nurse practitioners and registered nurses, rehabilitation therapists, clergy persons, pharmacists, other health care providers, and volunteers. Team members work collaboratively to assess a patient's needs and develop a care plan.	Older persons, many with complex medical and psychosocial issues, benefit from the input of multiple disciplines working together in an integrated manner.
Geriatric assessment	Comprehensive geriatric assessment is an important tool that can identify a broad range of functional impairments and their interaction with patients' underlying medical problems, home environments, and social support systems, allowing for early intervention and treatment.	As patients age, functional impairments (cognitive, physical, psychological, and social) can have a profound effect on their ability to maintain their health and to live independently in the community. Many of these impairments can be treated simply and inexpensively if they are identified early.
Culturally competent practice	Members of minority groups are projected to increase from 5.7 million in 2000 (16.4% of the elderly population) to 8.1 million in 2010 (20.1% of the elderly) and then to 12.9 million in 2020 (23.6% of the elderly) (AARP, 2005). As the United States becomes more ethnically diverse, health care providers must learn about the perspectives and values of a variety of cultural groups.	There are serious ramifications of ignoring the impact of cultural diversity in the delivery of health care services. When different cultures collide and are not recognized, acknowledged, and identified, common reactions of patient, family, and health care provider may include denial, depression, isolation, avoidance, fear, frustration, guilt, anger, and resentment.

(continued)

Core competency	Definition	Rationale
Palliative and end-of-life care	Palliative care focuses on relieving suffering and achieving the best possible quality of life for patients and their caregivers. It is offered simultaneously with life-prolonging therapies for persons living with serious, complex, and eventually terminal illness.	Palliative care improves the quality of life of patients and their families facing the problems associated with life-threatening illness. Prevention and relief of suffering is achieved by means of early identification, assessment, and treatment of pain and other physical, psychosocial, and spiritual issues.
Rural and medically underserved populations	Rural elderly tend to experience more functional limitations. In particular, rural nonfarm elders are found to report higher numbers of medical conditions, more functional limitations, and greater difficulty in performing tasks of daily living than all other residential categories. Medically underserved areas (MUAs) and medically underserved populations (MUPs) are designations for areas characterized by shortages of primary medical care, dental, or mental health providers (Health Services and Resources Administration, 2008).	Specific factors that have a negative impact on the health and welfare of the rural elder population include: lower levels of education, persistent poverty, geographic isolation, poor transportation, and lack of advocacy and supportive services.
Geriatric mental health	Older people are at increased risk of serious mental illness, particularly depression and anxiety, in the face of bereavement, living alone, weak social supports, anxiety, physical function deficits, and limitation of activities, all of which are exacerbated particularly for the elderly in times of disaster and trauma.	Specialized training of health care professionals and allied health care providers in mental health, and particularly mental health of older persons, is essential to meet the increasing heath needs of this growing population.
Continuum of care	The goal of structuring the continuum of care is to reduce fragmentation and lack of communication between health care providers, and to achieve safe and smooth transitions for older patients, within and across care settings.	There is increasing evidence about the importance of ensuring seamless transitions to ensure optimal patient outcomes (e.g., physical functioning, medication reconciliation, mental health).

TABLE 11.2
Special Training Topics

Topic	Definition	Rationale
Emergency preparedness	The elderly, especially frail and disabled older people, face extraordinary physical, emotional, and mental health challenges in the event of natural or manmade disaster.	The need for education and training related to bio-terrorism, emergency preparedness, and aging has become an important issue for health care providers of older adults in light of manmade (e.g., terrorist attacks) and natural recent events (e.g., Hurricane Katrina).
Elder mistreatment and neglect	It is estimated that approximately 4% of adults over the age of 65 are victims of elder abuse; furthermore, it is estimated that only 1 in 14 cases are reported.	The National Elder Abuse Incidence Study (NEAIS) indicates that approximately 450,000 older adults in domestic settings were abused or neglected in 1996.
Ethical and legal issues	The most common legal and ethical issues in geriatric care involve assessment of decisional capacity and competence, identification of decision-makers, resolution of conflicts about care, disclosure of information, termination of treatment at the end of life, and decisions about long-term care.	The delivery of ethical patient care is a goal of all health care providers. The task can be more challenging when an elderly patient has an array of conditions and diseases that drain physiologic, psychological, and social reserves, creating a greater risk of adverse outcomes.
Hazards of hospitalization	Complications may include reduced muscle strength, bone density, pulmonary function, and sensory function, with many older persons beginning an irreversible decline in terms of function and quality of life upon hospitalization (Creditor, 1993).	Hospitalization is very risky for older persons, particularly the very old. It can lead to serious functional decline that is unrelated to the reason for hospitalization.

(continued)

TABLE 11.2 (*continued*)

Polypharmacy	More than 40% of community-dwelling older persons take 5 or more different medications each week, with 12% taking 10 or more.	While medications are necessary to improve functioning and slow the progression of chronic diseases, this multiple drug use is associated with an elevated risk of adverse health outcomes resulting in hospitalizations and sometimes death.
Housing	The vast majority of elders desire to age in place, but this is not always possible. For those who must move, housing options are often not affordable or available, and there is a lack of integration between health and social services and housing.	Many older adults face traumatic and significant changes in their homes as they grow older, often facing substandard, isolated, and unaffordable housing options. It is imperative that health professionals in aging be cognizant of the many complex issues related to housing for the elderly and be aware of options and private and government subsidies and programs.

and direct care workers in the requisite knowledge, skills, and attitudes to provide patient/person-centered, evidence-based, and coordinated interdisciplinary geriatric care and aging services" (White House Conference on Aging, 2005, p.1). The only realistic approach to this formidable national training effort will be to employ the train-the-trainer educational model. This model is based on two principles: (a) adult learning theory, which states that people who train others remember 90% of the material they teach, and (b) diffusion of innovation theory, which holds that people adopt new information through their trusted social and professional networks. Thus, a series of the train-the-trainer programs in geriatric education would first develop cadres of skilled interdisciplinary community-based trainers, who in turn would train others in their community on how to integrate geriatric knowledge and skills into their practices.

Increasing Access to Health Care

It is projected that between 2000 and 2012 the need for health professionals will grow at twice the rate of all other occupations and that an estimated 29% more providers will be necessary. The uneven geographic distribution of the workforce will also continue to be an issue. Today, there are 4,474 health professional shortage areas (HPSAs) in the United States, in which 62 million people live and 35 million are underserved. The situation is particularly acute for older Americans living in rural areas, where it is difficult to attract, train, and retain health professionals (Goins, Gainor, Pollard, & Spencer, 2003). Offering geriatric training to community health providers will also address these projected workforce shortages and help to meet the health care needs of the rural elderly (Advisory Committee on Interdisciplinary and Community-Based Linkages, 2001).

Reducing Health Disparities

Racial and ethnic minorities tend to receive lower-quality health care than Whites, even when insurance status, income, age, and severity of conditions are comparable. These disparities, which have been thoroughly documented, represent a pressing national problem (Smedley, Stith, & Nelson, 2003). One solution for expanding access to quality health care is to increase the number of trained community health professionals in geriatrics, with special emphasis on the building the racial and ethnic diversity of the health care workforce. A diverse and culturally competent health care workforce will contribute to improved access for the underserved *and* the elderly (Cohen, Gabriel, & Terrell, 2002).

KEY GERIATRIC TRAINING PROGRAMS FOR
COMMUNITY HEALTH PROFESSIONALS

Government Supported Programs

Under Title VII of the Public Health Service Act, the Bureau of Health Professions provides funding for three key programs that provide interdisciplinary training in geriatric care for all health professions: (a) the Geriatric Education Centers (GECs) program; (b) the Geriatric Training Program for Physicians, Dentists, and Behavioral/Mental Health Professionals; and (c) the Geriatric Academic Career Awards (GACA) program. In addition to addressing the shortage of geriatric practitioners, these three initiatives increase access to quality health care, improve diversity of the health care workforce, and recruit and retain health care professionals in medically underserved areas.

Geriatric Education Centers (GECs)

GECs are the only federally funded programs geared solely to the education of health professionals in the diagnosis, treatment, and prevention of disease and other health concerns of the elderly. Initiated in 1985, there are currently 48 GECs, which provide training through continuing education, curriculum development and dissemination, training and retraining of faculty, and clinical training in geriatrics in nursing homes, chronic and acute disease hospitals, ambulatory care centers, and senior centers. Over the last two decades, achievements of the GEC program include:

> Training more than 50,000 health care professionals from 35 health-related disciplines to better serve the burgeoning older adult population.
>
> Developing over 2,500 curricular materials on aging-related topics, including interdisciplinary team care, geriatric syndromes, ethnogeriatrics, cultural competency, health literacy, quality of care, rural health access issues, and bioterrorism and emergency preparedness.
>
> Delivering 282 distance learning programs to 37,000 health care professionals in rural and underserved areas (Advisory Committee on Interdisciplinary and Community-Based Linkages, 2006).

The Geriatric Training Program for Physicians, Dentists, and Behavioral/Mental Health Professions

This program offers 1- or 2-year programs to train these professionals to become geriatric academicians. Programs provide fellows with exposure to elderly patients in various levels of wellness and functioning and from a range of socioeconomic and racial/ethnic backgrounds. Clinical rotations include geriatric consultation services, acute care services, dental services, geriatric psychiatry units, day and home care programs, rehabilitation services, extended care facilities, geriatric ambulatory care, and community care programs for elderly persons. This is the only program in the United States that trains faculty in postdoctoral geriatric dentistry (Advisory Committee on Interdisciplinary and Community-Based Linkages, 2001).

The Geriatric Academic Career Award (GACA)

The GACA program supports the academic career development of geriatricians in junior faculty positions who are committed to teaching geriatrics in medical schools across the country. GACA recipients are required to provide training in clinical geriatrics, including the training of interdisciplinary teams of health care professionals. Activities include curriculum development, serving on medical school curriculum committees, providing care and teaching in a wide range of clinical settings, clinical research, participating in educational programs to build their own skills, and providing continuing education to practicing health professionals of multiple disciplines as well as community workers, including police personnel, informal caregivers, and community-dwelling elderly persons (National Association of Geriatric Education Centers, n.d.). Many GACA recipients are currently implementing geriatric curricula in community-based settings (Advisory Committee on Interdisciplinary and Community-Based Linkages, 2006).

Geriatric Research, Education, and Clinical Centers (GRECCs) Program of the VA

The GRECCs were established in 1976 with a mission to enhance the quality of care of aging veterans through excellence in research, education, and clinical program development. The GRECCs host training programs in the allied health disciplines, including social work, nursing, pharmacy, and audiology, which expose students to an array of clinical experiences in geriatrics. They also are the home to geriatric fellowship programs, with the VA being the first to establish such fellowship training in geriatrics in 1978. The GRECCs and their host VA facilities have played a major historical role in geriatrics training and the preparation of future community-based practitioners.

Area Health Education Centers (AHECs) and Health Education Training Centers (HETCs) Programs

The AHEC program was established in 1971 to recruit, train, and retain a health professions workforce committed to underserved populations. The HETC program was created in 1989 to provide programs for specific populations with persistent, severe unmet health needs. Together the AHEC and HETC programs help bring the resources of academic medicine to bear in addressing local community health needs. Today, 50 AHEC programs with more than 200 centers and a dozen HETCs exist in most states, with approximately 120 medical schools and 600 nursing and allied health schools working collaboratively with AHECs and HETCs to improve health for underserved and underrepresented populations (Warshaw & Bragg, 2003).

Impact of Federal Budgetary Constraints
In 2005 Title VII training programs were eliminated from the federal budget, resulting in closeouts of GECs, GACAs, the geriatric fellowships, and many other programs funded under Title VII. This was a significant setback to the geriatrics training movement, resulting in the closing of many GECs throughout the nation and the termination of training for scores of physicians, mental health professionals and dentists being trained through GACAs and fellowships. The network of geriatric health professional advocates mobilized to fight these budget cuts, and Title VII funding was restored for these programs in fiscal year 2007. However, the impact was serious in that some grantees were unable to marshal the resources to reapply for funding. Furthermore, the funding cycles have been shortened from 5 to 3 years, severely truncating the program cycle for GECs and the leadership training activities of individual grantees under the GACAs and fellowships.

Privately Funded Training Initiatives
Many current advances in geriatrics education and workforce preparation are attributable to sustained philanthropic support from the John A. Hartford Foundation and the Donald W. Reynolds Foundation.

John A. Hartford Foundation (JAHF)
The goal of JAHF is to increase the nation's capacity to provide effective and affordable care to its rapidly increasing older population (The John A. Hartford Foundation, 2008). The foundation has assumed a national leadership role in the training of physicians, nurses, and social workers in the care of older adults through several grant initiatives, including the Geriatric Interdisciplinary Team Training program geared toward enhanced interprofessional collaboration in the care of older adults. Selected Hartford Foundation projects

that directly or indirectly promote geriatric training for community health providers include the following.

Hartford Centers of Excellence. The strategy of the Centers of Excellence initiative is to identify medical schools with the necessary components for training academic geriatricians, such as research infrastructure, advanced training opportunities, and academic mentoring, and then offer financial resources to these institutions to train larger numbers of future faculty more rapidly than would otherwise be possible. Since the inception of this program in 1997, the 24 Hartford-designated Centers of Excellence have produced hundreds of geriatric-expert leaders in medical research, education, and practice. Centers of Excellence have also helped to create a higher level of recognition and appreciation of the discipline throughout their respective medical centers, universities, and affiliated clinical service settings, thereby encouraging physicians in almost all medical specialties to become more knowledgeable about age-related health issues. Centers of Excellence also produce clinician educators who are qualified to teach primary care physicians and specialists practicing in the community about specific care issues regarding their older patients.

Reaching Primary Care Providers: Practicing Physician Education (PPE) in Geriatrics Program. With a shift from acute care to chronic care needs with the aging of the population, an increasing number of older adults are receiving care from community-based primary care providers. Among innovative approaches to infuse geriatrics in the practices of office-based practitioners is the PPE in Geriatrics program, initiated by the JAHF and the American Geriatrics Society in 1997. Based on a needs assessment conducted by the American College of Physicians and the American Academy of Family Physicians, toolkits were developed on topics such as memory loss, depression, and urinary incontinence. Community-based, generalist physicians were selected and trained to serve as peer educators in their communities. The training sessions were led by geriatrician clinical educators who instructed the community-based physicians to facilitate nonhierarchical, case-based and active mode learning sessions based on the topic-specific toolkits. These sessions on memory loss, depression, and urinary incontinence were held at community sites such as hospitals, clinics, group practice offices, and local physician meetings. During a 3-year period, 1,309 community-based providers were trained, with community physicians reporting increased knowledge in the areas of memory loss and urinary incontinence (Levine et al., 2007).

John A. Hartford Foundation Institute for Geriatric Nursing. In 1996 the JAHF turned its focus for the first time to a major nursing initiative, with a grant to create the John A. Hartford Foundation Institute for Geriatric Nursing at New York University. The institute, dedicated to promoting the highest level of geriatric competence in all nurses, has led a national effort to integrate geriatric content into nursing school curricula, as well as adding geriatric topics to in-service nursing education for those already in the workforce (The John A. Hartford Foundation, 2008).

Geriatric Social Work Initiative. The JAHF Geriatric Social Work Initiative collaborates with social work education programs to prepare social workers to help improve the care and well-being of older adults and their families. Specifically, the initiative develops excellent training opportunities in real-world settings through the Practicum Partnership Program, which offers excellent community field education models to future practitioners, many of whom will be community providers (Geriatric Social Work Initiative, 2008).

Donald Reynolds Foundation

The Reynolds Foundation is also committed to improving the quality of life of America's growing older population through increased training of physicians in geriatrics. The Aging and Quality of Life program was established in 2000 by the foundation in response to a growing consensus that most physicians lack adequate training to specifically meet the increasing needs of the frail elderly patient. Such patients typically suffer from multiple, interactive physical and psychosocial conditions—both acute and chronic—that compromise their capacity to function in daily life and lessen their independence. The Reynolds Foundation has committed almost $60 million to a total of 30 different training institutions under this initiative and will award an additional $20 million to 10 additional institutions within calendar year 2007 (Donald W. Reynolds Foundation, 2008).

TRAINING PROGRAMS, METHODS, AND CLINICAL SETTINGS

Training opportunities for community-based health professionals in geriatrics and gerontology are available nationwide under the auspices of many different types of educational institutions including health professional schools, colleges, universities, community colleges, and junior colleges. Depending on the focus of the training initiative, programs are offered to a range of health care disciplines including physicians, nurses, nurse practitioners, social workers, chaplains, nutritionists, pharmacists, psychologists, and physical therapists. Although graduate degrees with specialization in geriatrics are offered by academic institutions, community based health professionals often prefer certificate programs that offer flexibility. Certification is a voluntary process that allows an individual to demonstrate specialized knowledge, practice principles, and skills required in a practice discipline that are consistent with nationally specified quality standards and values. Certification differs from licensing in that it is a voluntary process that is usually offered through professional organizations. Licensing is a governmental process that gives an individual permission to practice in a particular state (Howe et al., 2007).

Training methods incorporate the principles of adult learning theory and are based on classroom-based learning methods (e.g., seminars, workshops, institutes, and conferences) interactive approaches (e.g., case discussions, journal article analyses, and role-playing), and clinical experiences as discussed later in this chapter.

Longitudinal training experiences in a variety of clinical settings are critical in geriatrics so that learners understand the nature of chronic and acute illnesses and their effects on an older person's day-to-day life, functional status, and overall quality of life, as well as the perils of transitions. In some areas of the country, community health centers (CHCs) and rural health centers are important venues for geriatric health care education. Interdisciplinary clinical sites are optimal but are more challenging to organize because of the need to engage learners at different levels and from different disciplines.

An interdisciplinary faculty and team-teaching format models the importance of interdisciplinary teamwork and exposes trainees to diverse and rich perspectives in assessing and caring for older patients. The VA pioneered interprofessional education, beginning with the Interdisciplinary Team Training Program in the 1980s and currently funded programs such as the GRECC Allied Health Training Program and the Interprofessional Palliative Care and Psychology Fellowship Programs. The challenge of an interdisciplinary training program is to make learning dynamic and interactive and the content relevant to all disciplines (Howe, Mellor, & Cassel, 1999). Despite the challenges, however, the benefits far outweigh any disadvantages because of the cross-fertilization of ideas, knowledge, perspectives, and skills (Howe, Hyer, Mellor, Lindeman, & Luptak, 2001).

Access to continuing education has historically been a problem for health care professionals in rural areas because of the distances they must travel to attend classes and meetings. Not surprisingly, geriatric training opportunities also tend to be clustered in urban locales, making it more difficult for rural providers to receive training (Malone, Poon, & Shetterly, 1998). The GECs have pioneered the use of technology, in part, to help close this educational opportunity gap by hosting online training programs and videoconferencing capability.

Service-learning is a "teaching and learning strategy that integrates meaningful community service with instruction and reflection to enrich the learning experience, teach civic responsibility, and strengthen communities" (Learn and Serve Clearinghouse, 2008). More and more students and community partners are participating in service-learning experiences in the areas of gerontology and geriatrics. The types of service-learning projects are wide-ranging, as are the potential benefits to students and community agencies. In general, service-learning programs are driven by the needs and problems facing the community, not determined by the needs of an academic institution (Clark, 1999).

CURRICULUM

Specialized training in gerontology and geriatrics is essential for health care professionals to meet the complex health care demands of the aging baby boom generation. In addition, it is essential that this workforce understand the diversity of the older population with respect to race, ethnicity, gender, lifestyle, and income. Trainees must also be prepared to work on interdisciplinary teams in an array of settings, as well as a variety of organizational environments, including managed care and vertically integrated health systems. And with the shift to community and home-based care, geriatric care coordination and managing potentially risky transitions along the care continuum have emerged as essential skill sets.

Tailoring the Curriculum to the Needs of Learners

Curricular standards are often set by panels of experts with input from professional organizations and leaders in the field. They list and categorize the knowledge, skills, and attitudes necessary to attain competence in that particular field. For example, the Education Committee of the American Geriatrics Society has published a set of core competencies for the care of the older patient (American Geriatrics Society, 2000). However, trainees learn best in the context of what they feel they need to know in order to provide competent care. It may be just as important, therefore, to understand trainees' perceived deficits in their knowledge and skills, and what barriers trainees identify when providing care to older patients (Drickamer, Levy, Irwin, & Rohrbaugh, 2006). The importance of curricular needs assessment was illustrated by a survey of community primary care physicians, which revealed that practicing clinicians were more interested in learning about geriatric management than diagnosis,

TABLE 11.3

Strategies for Training Community-Based Providers in Geriatrics

Strategies	Rationale
Plan for sustainability of the national training effort	Partnerships among educational institutions, service providers, foundations, and government should continue to collaborate to address the critical need for a geriatric health care workforce.
Faculty development	Train-the-trainer models should be expanded to enable a larger cadre of trainers to bring geriatrics to community health providers.
Service-learning programs	These academic-community partnerships expose learners to community-based settings and link the needs of community-residing individuals with academic institutions.
Expand distance learning capability	Distance learning methods (e.g., video and audio conferences and Web-based learning) increase the access of rural providers to new knowledge in geriatrics.
Career ladders and opportunities	Put greater focus on career opportunities and career ladders for community health providers in geriatrics (e.g., adjunct faculty appointments).
Identify feasible and effective evaluation methods	Assessing the impact of community providers on the health and well-being of older adults will provide the data needed for new program development and funding incentives to increase the workforce.
Continuing education opportunities	Community providers need training that is flexible in its format, prerequisites, and time slots.
Target nontraditional students	Adult, nontraditional students need to be identified as potential aging service workers.
Incentives to increase recruitment of new practitioners into geriatric practice	Government incentives in the form of education loan forgiveness have been proposed in the United States Congress (e.g., Senate Bill No. 2708) to attract and retain providers in geriatrics through loan forgiveness and other career-advancement opportunities.
System fragmentation	Workforce training is fragmented across governmental entities and academic and clinical settings. A comprehensive approach is needed to identify gaps and opportunities.
Develop alternative financial support strategies	In order to increase sustainability, the geriatric training effort must reduce reliance on single funding sources (e.g., federal DHHS/BHP/HRSA) and diversify (e.g., states).

especially of dementia, multiple comorbidities, and depression (Williams & Connolly, 1990).

POLICY RECOMMENDATIONS AND FUTURE DIRECTIONS

The need for trained community health professionals in geriatrics is a critically important but complex national challenge that can only be met by the coordinated efforts of a national partnership of academicians, politicians, advocates for the elderly, health policy experts, and philanthropic foundations. See Table 11.3 for highlights of strategies and future directions.

CONCLUSION

This chapter has reviewed the education and training programs that have been developed and implemented in an effort to increase the number of community health providers serving older adults in the United States. Geriatric training programs for physicians, nurses, social workers, pharmacists, and other allied health professionals have been developed in a range of clinical, community, and academic settings. These include university- and VA-sponsored training programs with classroom and clinical components at sites such as inpatient units, outpatient clinics, long-term care facilities, and community and home care programs. Furthermore, there have been targeted efforts to prepare future clinicians with expertise in geriatrics through national training initiatives, including federally supported programs (e.g., GECs, GACAs, Medicare support of geriatrics fellowships), VA GRECC allied health and geriatrics training programs, and initiatives supported by foundations such as the John A. Hartford and Donald W. Reynolds Foundations. However, despite the recognition of the need for geriatric training of community health providers, and the programs that have been developed to date, there is still a pressing need for increased public and private funding and the pursuit of strategies such as those outlined in this chapter.

REFERENCES

AARP. (2005). *Profile of older Americans*. Retrieved March 14, 2008, from http://assets. aarp.org/rgcenter/general/profile_2005.pdf

Advisory Committee on Interdisciplinary and Community-Based Linkages. (2001). *First report to the secretary, DHHS*. Retrieved January 22, 2008, from http://bhpr. hrsa.gov/interdisciplinary/acicbl/reports/first/c5.htm

Advisory Committee on Interdisciplinary and Community-Based Linkages. (2006). *Minutes from July 24–25, 2006 meeting.* Retrieved January 22, 2008, from http:// bhpr.hrsa.gov/interdisciplinary/acicbl/072406minutes.htm

American Geriatrics Society. (2000). Core competencies for the care of older patients: Recommendations of the American Geriatrics Society. *Academic Medicine, 75*(3), 252–255.

American Geriatrics Society. (2005). *Letter to the centers for Medicare and Medicaid Services.* Retrieved March 14, 2008, from http:// www.americangeriatrics. org/news/letters_dept.shtml

American Geriatrics Society Core Writing Group of the Task Force on the Future of Geriatric Medicine. (2005). Caring for older Americans: The future of geriatric medicine. *Journal of the American Geriatrics Society, 53,* 5245–5415.

Americans for Nursing Shortage Relief. (2007). *Consensus document.* Retrieved March 25, 2008, from http:// www.ncgnp.org/associations/814/files/Consensus Document.pdf

Clark, P. G. (1999). Service-learning education in community-academic partnerships: Implications for interdisciplinary geriatric raining in the health professions. *Educational Gerontology, 25,* 641–660.

Cohen J. J., Gabriel, B. A., & Terrell, C. (2002). The case for diversity in the health care workforce. *Health Affairs, 21*(5), 90–102.

Creditor, M. C. (1993). Hazards of hospitalization of the elderly. *Annals of Internal Medicine, 118*(3), 219–223.

Department of Health and Human Services. (2007a). *Administration on Aging. A profile of older Americans.* Retrieved March 27, 2008, from http:// www.aoa.gov/pROF/ Statistics/profile/2007/14.asp

Department of Health and Human Services. (2007b). *DHHS, BHP, HRSA, Geriatric Education Center Grant Program guidance.* New announcement, HRSA-07-108, Catalog of Federal Domestic Assistance No. 93.949. Issued April 9, 2007.

Donald W. Reynolds Foundation. (2008). *Aging and quality of life.* Retrieved March 27, 2008, from http://www.dwreynolds.org/programs/national/aging/aboutAging. htm

Drickamer, M. A., Levy, B., Irwin, K. S., & Rohrbaugh, R. M. (2006). Perceived needs for geriatric education by medical students, internal medicine residents and faculty. *Journal of General Internal Medicine, 21*(12), 1230–1234.

Geriatric Social Work Initiative. (2008). *Preparing social workers for an aging population.* Retrieved March 20, 2008, from http://www.gswi.org/about/about.html

Goins, R. T., Gainor, S. J., Pollard, C., & Spencer, S. M. (2003). Geriatric knowledge and educational needs among rural health care professionals. *Educational Gerontology, 29,* 261–272.

Health Resources and Services Administration. (2008). *Find shortage areas: MUA/P by state and country.* Retrieved February 27, 2008, from http://www.muafind.hrsa.gov

Howe, J. L., Bowen, L., Frank, J., Maiden, R., McBride, M., St. Hill, H., et al. (2007). *Environmental scan report: Certification in the field of gerontology.* Report prepared for the Executive Committee of the Association of Gerontology in Higher Education.

Howe, J. L., Mellor, M. J., & Cassel, C. K. (1999). Cross-disciplinary approaches to teaching interdisciplinary teamwork and geriatrics. *Gerontology and Geriatrics Education, 19*(4), 3–17.

Howe, J. L., Hyer, K., Mellor, J., Lindeman, D., & Luptak, M. (2001). Educational approaches for preparing social work students for interdisciplinary teamwork on geriatric health care teams. *Social Work in Health Care, 32*(4), 19–42.

John A. Hartford Foundation. (2008). *About us.* Retrieved March 20, 2008, from http://www.jhartfound.org

Lawhorne, L. (2005). Care of the older adult in the office setting. *Primary Care: Clinics in Office Practice, 32*(3), xi–xiv.

Learn and Serve Clearinghouse. (2008). *What is service learning?* Retrieved March 26, 2008, from http://www.servicelearning.org

Levine, S. A., Robinson, B. E., Stratos, G. A., Lascher, S. M., Goodwin, C., Dunn, K., et al. (2007). Practicing physician education in geriatrics: Lessons learned from a train-the-trainer model. *Journal of the American Geriatrics Society, 55*(8), 1281–1286.

Malone, D. M., Poon, L. W., & Shetterly, K. (1998). Assessing training needs of geriatric service providers: Program rationale and focus group outcomes. *Educational Gerontology, 24,* 639–654.

National Association of Geriatric Education Centers. (n.d.). *Legislative priorities.* Retrieved March 25, 2008, from http://www.nagec.org/legislative/default.asp

Resnick, B. (2007). An alternative solution to our shortage of nurses, physicians, pharmacists, and other health care providers? *Geriatric Nursing, 28*(4), 207–209.

Smedley, B. D., Stith, A. Y., & Nelson, A. R. (Eds.). (2003). *Unequal treatment: Confronting racial and ethnic disparities in health care.* Committee on Understanding and Eliminating Racial and Ethnic Disparities in Health Care, Institute of Medicine. Washington, DC: The National Academics Press.

Warshaw, G. A., & Bragg, E. J. (2003). The training of geriatricians in the United States: Three decades of progress. *Journal of the American Geriatrics Society, 51*(7 Suppl.), S338–S345.

White House Conference on Aging. (2005). *Final report and recommendations by the Mini-Conference on Geriatric Health Care Workforce Issues, July 16, 2005.* Retrieved September 29, 2008, from http://www.americangeriatrics.org/policy/WHCoAMini Conf_090705.pdf

Williams M. E., & Connolly, N. K. (1990). What practicing physicians in North Carolina rate as their most challenging geriatric medicine concerns. *Journal of the American Geriatrics Society, 38,* 1230–1234.

CHAPTER 12

Education About Special Aging Populations

Intellectually Disabled, Incarcerated, and Non-English-Speaking

Anthony A. Sterns and Edward F. Ansello

The age wave is having a broad effect in many ways everywhere that people live throughout the world. But that age wave is composed of many special groups and, like a pier jutting into the ocean, the underpinnings are always being challenged and tested. Special populations test the robustness of theories on aging and on models for delivery of services to aging individuals. It is with these special groups that many professional challenges arise and the opportunity for creativity emerges.

When information flows out from work with these special groups to the general aging population, opportunities for new approaches to benefit the broader worldview can be realized. From the perspective of the gerontological educator, special populations offer the chance to demonstrate the generalizability of theory. At the same time, it can be a continuous source of new ideas and approaches to provide additional synergy to models of service delivery for older adults and people with disabilities. As the age wave begins to challenge the resources of the world available to serve, mitigate, support, and comfort adults and older adults, those serving these special populations are acting as scouts to ferret out the best strategies to efficiently and effectively meet both the special needs and the common needs of older adults.

185

DOI: 10.1891/0198-8794.28.185

In this chapter we will examine three special populations in detail. The first will be those individuals who are facing age-related challenges with an intellectual or developmental disability. We will then look at older inmates who are faced with the challenges of aging while incarcerated. Last we will examine those individuals who are in need of services but do not speak the native language of the country where they live. In each of these cases we will look at the impact of the age wave, the unique challenges of aging for each special population, and the theories and approaches that are being used to deliver services to this population and that are being applied to the general older adult population.

Our intention is to present the background information necessary to present basic information about the subject and relevant theoretical perspectives important to developing and delivering services to that special population. With the background and theory, examples of successful field applications are presented, and we suggest how those applications are relevant to the general elderly population.

AGING WITH INTELLECTUAL AND DEVELOPMENTAL DISABILITIES

Description of the Population

The survival to later life of large numbers of individuals with formerly life-stunting developmental disabilities, such as cerebral palsy, autism, and intellectual disabilities, is a relatively recent phenomenon, one that has caught both aging and developmental disabilities systems off guard; yet there are at least a half million individuals age 60 and above with these disabilities (Ansello, 2004). There is little established training protocol, insufficient numbers of service providers cross-trained in aging and developmental disabilities, and scant articulated public policy regarding the needs, capacities, or challenges of older adults with lifelong disabilities (with the exception of the Rehabilitation Research and Training Center, 2008). Complicating the matter, there is evidence that those who are currently older (ages 50 or above) with lifelong developmental disabilities are qualitatively different from their younger counterparts in a number of ways. One major difference is residential status. Those older individuals tend to reside more in family or small-group residential settings than independently. Another difference is the incorporation of self-advocacy skills. Those who are older tend, because of their earlier birth dates, to have benefited less from mainstreaming education and various federal and state legislative actions intended to strengthen self-care and self-advocacy.

The majority of today's older adults with lifelong disabilities have lived their lives in the community either in the care of their parents or in regular contact with them, because these parents were disappointed by the medical and social services communities in their time of greatest need when their children were born (i.e., during the 1950s and 1960s). These parents became effective protectors of and advocates for their children. Their grassroots initiatives led ultimately to the national movements and organizations we are familiar with today. Because of the greater numbers of children with mental retardation (more properly called intellectual disabilities today), mental retardation-related programs and practices often dominate discussions of lifelong developmental disabilities. Irrespective of the particular name of the lifelong disability, the sustaining continuity of caregiving by parents and families has been a major contributor to the survival to later life of greater numbers of persons with lifelong disabilities. Consequently, when considering aging with lifelong disabilities at present, one must keep in mind the aging adult and the caregiving family, in other words, a two-generation geriatric context (Ansello & Janicki, 2000). At the same time, those who are older with lifelong disabilities tend to be survivors, relatively quite capable, higher-functioning adults. Therefore, outreach, teaching, and services to the oldest of today's older adults with lifelong disabilities should always consider this interwoven relationship.

Persons with lifelong disabilities, as we have noted in Janicki and Ansello (2000), share with their counterparts without such disabilities the common need for dignity, respect for individuality, and supportive services to help maintain a level of relative autonomy. Supportive services, in this instance, may include advocacy, adult protective services, personal assistance services, alternative living arrangements, transportation (which we focus on later in this chapter), social, medical, and recreational services, services couched within a well-planned and coordinated interagency framework, and (always) services from appropriately trained staff. At the same time, however, there are some special needs particular to populations with disabilities that they do not share with mainstream American elders and that have not been adequately addressed through current service system structures. These include peer socialization opportunities, community exposure/involvement, involvement in services and activities included in the generic aging system, access to day program services that provide skill development and interventions designed to sustain an individual's current skill level, family living and small group situations with appropriate accommodations to changing individual needs, exercise, nutritional counseling, and other health-promoting physical activities for health maintenance, leisure time, and recreational activities appropriate to disability and aging impairment levels, and so forth.

A developmental disability as defined by the Developmental Disabilities Assistance and Bill of Rights Act (2000), as amended, is a severe, chronic disability that is attributable to a mental or physical impairment or combination of mental and physical impairments that manifest before age 22, that is likely to continue indefinitely and results in at least three substantial functional limitations, and that reflects the person's need for a combination of services that are lifelong or of extended duration.

The definition relates to functional abilities, not to categorical labeling. Therefore, lifelong, developmental disabilities applies to a broad spectrum of conditions and *may* include individuals with intellectual disabilities, cerebral palsy, autism, blindness, deafness, neurological impairments, orthopedic handicaps, multiple disabilities, and other lifelong disabilities resulting from spinal cord injuries, trauma to the head, or other accidents that occurred before age 22. The largest subgroup of individuals with lifelong, developmental disabilities consists of persons with intellectual disabilities, usually defined as those individuals with significantly below average general intellectual functioning (Goldmeier & Herr, 1999; Janicki & Ansello, 2000). At the same time, levels of functioning may well depend on environmental and interpersonal supports or barriers.

Many persons with mild intellectual disabilities are often not considered disadvantaged in certain environments. And so the definitional paradigm is shifting to one that is multidimensional, recognizing functional skills, individualized supports, personal well-being, and personal competence that is enhanced through environmental modification, skills acquisition, and use of prosthetics (Schalock & Luckasson, 2004). This is not mere semantics but rather a fundamental reorientation in what makes a person "disabled." Clearly, this has implications for the form and substance of training, teaching, and services for persons with lifelong disabilities.

Theories on Aging and Approaches to Service

The key theory and principles in applications and service approaches are normalization, assisted autonomy, and heterogeneity. We describe each in turn.

Normalization

Normalization, also called social role valorization, is the prevailing ethic guiding assistance for persons with developmental disabilities. First articulated by Wolfensberger (1972), normalization emphasizes the basic human rights of individuals with lifelong disabilities, such as the right to live, work, and exercise choice in the community. Normalization, in turn, has led to the guiding philosophy of inclusion or integrating people with lifelong disabilities into the lifeblood and daily functioning of the community. So-called mainstreaming legislation, like the Education for All Handicapped Children Act of 1975 helped to integrate persons with lifelong disabilities early in the life course (Goldmeier & Herr, 1999). These persons are now midlife adults.

The values of normalization and inclusion lead directly to the principles of empowerment. Empowerment for persons with lifelong disabilities rests on enabling actions that serve to recognize and give voice to the individual behind the disability. Goldmeier and Herr (1999) enumerate key principles of empowerment, including: respecting expressed preferences and demonstrated needs; ensuring accessibility and availability of supportive services; committing to mutual dedication to problem-solving, actively engaging the person with the lifelong disability; using consumers' wisdom and experience; generating creative interventions or responding with new approaches as age and circumstance modify needs; enacting leadership as a dual process involving the service provider and the individual with disabilities; and practicing patience.

Assisted Autonomy

Assisted autonomy (Ansello & Janicki, 2000) describes the reality that individuals with lifelong disabilities may become relatively more fully integrated and functioning through the assistance of others. Independence is seldom achievable at any point in the life-course, and may be even less so with age or impairments. Interdependence more truly describes one who is engaged with community and others, and is, therefore, more aligned with normalization for persons with lifelong disabilities. As Moody (1992) has noted, too often autonomy-as-independence fails to consider the deeper human need for respect and social connections, because "dignity is far more bound up with the interpersonal and social fabric than with isolated acts of rational deliberation or consent" (Moody, 1992, p. 4). Moreover, for the exercise of choice by individuals with lifelong disabilities to be meaningful, that is, for there to be true selection among options and true steps to activate the options selected, it will likely require some negotiation with and assistance from others. Thus, assisted autonomy rather than independence is a means to empowerment and inclusion.

Heterogeneity

A much-underappreciated reality of the human life-course is that people tend in most, if not all, ways to become less like their age mates as they grow older.

In the functioning of body organs, problem-solving, economic self-sufficiency, the metabolism of medications, and myriad other ways within-group variance tends to be greater in older samples than in their younger counterparts. This gerontological imperative of individuation, becoming more like oneself and less like others in one's cohort, is hardly a prosaic fantasy; rather it is simply the product of accumulating years of idiosyncratic life experiences whose net effect is to further and further differentiate group membership. Importantly, this imperative does not seem to disappear in the presence of lifelong disabilities (Ansello & Janicki, 2000). There is much behavioral variability, for instance, among different individuals who have similar IQ scores, reflecting their individual development, family and community supports, schooling, life experiences, adult responsibilities, and more.

Older adults with lifelong disabilities constitute a remarkably heterogeneous group overall, and within subgroups (e.g., those with cerebral palsy or those with Down syndrome), this diversity continues. Simply, the processes of human aging produce individuation or increased heterogeneity within a group as its membership ages. No one-size-fits-all service strategy or training technique applies.

Education Approaches to Support Services

Drawing on the experiences of adults with developmental disabilities, Mahon and Mactavish (2000) enumerate practices that activate a sense of belonging or inclusion. Conceptually, these practices help transform service or teaching systems into effective facilitators of assisted autonomy. Expressed as helpful guidelines, they recommend that the teacher or service provider:

1. Be committed to developing the strengths of those involved.
2. Place the person in a more active rather than a passive role.
3. Activate a role that encourages the participant to engage in problem-solving and self-direction.
4. Minimize social exclusion in general but focus on individualized teaching.
5. Recognize within-group variance or heterogeneity.
6. Consider both rehabilitation and habilitation approaches—that is, offer teaching or services both to prepare for a potential vocation and to adapt to current realities.

Poe and Edwards (2002) have developed teaching and training techniques that are based on many years of working with adults with intellectual disabilities in group residential and other settings. Their suggestions may readily generalize to other groups of would-be employees, students, or clients. Again, Mahon and Mactavish's (2000) principles of belonging are the underlying foundation; the person with a lifelong disability is a partner in the learning or service activity, not a passive recipient. Some agencies refer to this person as the "consumer" to convey the interactive nature of marketing and consumer choice, and perhaps something of the adage that the customer is always right. Poe and Edwards (2002) have a brief handbook to orient employees who are new to the intellectual disabilities service system. Its recommendations include, and go beyond, the following:

1. Organize learners into small groups, while maintaining a focus on each individual with person-centered planning.
2. Conduct a task analysis—that is, break each desired behavioral or skills outcome into its constituent parts, starting with the most basic task.
   a. Explain steps to be learned in concrete rather than abstract terms; even individuals with more involved intellectual disabilities can learn basics that can be built upon.
   b. Recognize and reward progress; verbal praise is seldom overused.
   c. Repeat and practice tasks that have been learned.
   d. Employ multimodal instruction techniques (e.g., saying the words of a task while doing the actions).

Adjust pacing to the needs of the small group and, further, to the needs of the individuals within that group; at the same time, go beyond the learner's verbal assurance that he or she has acquired what was to be learned. Persons with intellectual disabilities are often people pleasers, meaning that they will say what the questioner wants to hear. Their reliance on others in a supportive environment, their need for assisted autonomy, may condition them to wish to please their helpers, not wanting to let them down. Verify that a task has truly been learned. At the same time, service providers and teachers might themselves benefit from adjusting their own need to push ahead with the next task or the next objective. Communication with individuals with lifelong disabilities has a pace of its own. Everyone involved needs to adjust to its timing, being partners in the process.

Travel training offers a good example of how the principles of Mahon and Mactavish (2000) and Poe and Edwards (2002) can be applied for adults and older adults with intellectual challenges. Travel training is also an application that can serve as a model for older adults in general who need to stop driving because of age-related declines in cognitive or physical functioning and need to utilize other means of transportation to maintain their independence.

We begin a brief explanation of what travel training is and research that supports its success.

The Case of Travel Training

Over a period of more than 20 years, a knowledge base for designing accessible transportation has been established. One concept that has come to the forefront is *accessibility for all persons,* which purports a design that operates transportation services easily for use by all persons and in tandem improves transportation services for disabled users as well. Another issue that has evolved is the notion of the trip chain or linkage that links various services and modes of transportation together to provide an accessible and successful journey for persons with disabilities and the elderly (e.g., home to curb, curb to vehicle, vehicle transport to destination and entrance into building; Suen & Mitchell, 1993).

The term *travel training* refers to "self-paced, short-term, comprehensive, intensive instruction designed to teach" persons with cognitive or physical disabilities to travel safely and independently using public transportation services (National Information Center for Children and Youth with Disabilities, 1966). The first information on travel training to appear in the literature dealt with the transition of people with mental retardation from institutional to independent-living settings (e.g., residence or group homes; Tobias, 1963). This constituted a great leap from once providing complete care to teaching the many skills needed to gain a measure of self-sufficiency. In addition to essential skills (e.g., self-care, cleaning, cooking, and laundry), pedestrian and community navigation skills were now being viewed as necessary for becoming truly independent.

Travel training programs began in the late 1960s as public transportation systems were in the latter stages of transition from private to public ownership and control. Following passage of the U.S. Rehabilitation Act of 1973 and other laws, social service programming for people with disabilities grew.

As programming grew, social service professionals began to recognize public transportation as a valuable community resource that could benefit their clients. As a result, with the special challenges that persons with disabilities may have, travel training programs developed across the country as agencies began to take advantage of the mobility that public transportation could provide for their clients.

The first book on travel training, *Travel Instruction for the Handicapped,* was written by Laus (1977). Prior to 1990, information on travel training was scarce, with the exception of passing references made in other writings or an occasional report.

Several travel training models have emerged over the years to teach people how to use various forms of public transportation. Each model evolved to meet needs of specific groups:

1. Orientation and mobility training for the blind.
2. Educational model for travel training for the mentally retarded and developmentally disabled (MR/DD) used by schools and later adapted in some MR/DD agencies for adults.
3. Travel training models developed in response to the Americans With Disabilities Act (1990).
4. Transit models driven by the public transportation industry such as customer service travel training, companion training, and familiarity training.

Examples of Field Successes

To address the barriers and challenges of independent travel for persons with disabilities and to help them execute safe travel planning, there has been movement toward enacting legislation and establishing standards requiring accessible transportation (i.e., U.S. Rehabilitation Act of 1973, section 504; 1190 U.S. Americans with Disabilities Act [1990]). Project ACTION since 1988 has been active in travel training, dissemination of information, and providing funding for cooperative demonstration projects by public transportation providers to address the travel needs of persons with disabilities. Travel training is most utilized by adults including about 16% of trainees who are over the age of 50 (Sterns, Mattern, Sterns, & Wright-Penov, 2003).

Sterns and others conducted a study in cooperation with the County of Summit Board of Mental Retardation and Developmental Disabilities (CSBMR/DD) Department of Travel Training in Akron, Ohio (Sterns et al., 2003). The CSBMR/DD Department of Travel Training has conducted travel training for people with mental retardation and developmental disabilities since 1973.

The study approach was two-tiered. First, new measures of training satisfaction, independence, bus behavior, and quality of life were developed and gathered in an interview. A parallel interview containing similar measures of satisfaction, independence, and quality of life were obtained from parents or legal guardians. Second, historical data from past assessments was gathered and integrated into the interview database for evaluation.

The travel training curriculum and programming of the CSBMR/DD includes assessment, instruction, field sessions, practice, hands-on transit, feedback, prompting and reinforcement. A survey of CSBMR/DD travel training program participants provided efficient measurements indicating that training in independent travel is successful in providing a less restrictive environment for persons with disabilities.

This study demonstrated the success of teaching travel skills to cognitively and physically disabled persons. It clearly showed the connection to specific training skill areas. The training skill areas are based on orientation and mobility principles (LaGrow, 1990). The study showed that travel training works very well for both clients who receive travel training and for their parents and guardians.

Differences were found between the group in training for the first time and those who were being retrained. These differences likely reflected programmatic improvements within the travel training program. These changes included revisions to the assessment instrument that helped focus on specific training skills. Skills such as communicating with others, using numbers and making calculations related to purchases, time awareness, and traffic safety are particularly stronger in the group assessed for initial training. Differences might also represent the selection of individuals with more skills, who are more likely to find employment and qualify for training, especially in challenging economic times. Further differences could reflect the travel experience achieved by use of bus service of participants who are in for training simply for a new job location.

Improvements in a number of the skills examined in the interview were found. Problem-solving and environmental skills improved significantly. Problem-solving skills focus on what actions individual must take if they miss their bus or stop. Environmental skills relate to what actions individuals should take when they are out after dark or when the weather changes for the worse. These skills are focused on in the training and are more likely to be new to individuals traveling to a place of employment for the first time or to a person who is working a different shift.

Travel training contributes significantly to feelings of independence and a better quality of life. Persons trained took more trips compared with those who were only assessed. Individuals who successfully completed travel training were more likely to use fixed-route or paratransit services than those individuals who were only assessed. The assessed individuals were more likely than the travel-trained group to use group home or agency van services for activities outside their residence.

Satisfaction in independent travel was high among the travel-trained group. The majority of the trained METRO riders stated that they felt safe when traveling by themselves. With only few exceptions, trained individuals felt safe when traveling by public transit. They attributed this sense of safety to the travel training they had received through the community travel program of the CSBMR/DD.

Satisfaction with travel before training was mixed. Over one-fourth of the individuals indicated that they were unhappy with the way they were traveling prior to being travel trained. Individuals who were travel trained generally felt that they had the skills required to travel independently. They made good use of landmarks and possessed high problem-solving skills. Pedestrian skill levels were high among the travel trained who possessed the skills required to handle environmental challenges such as inclement weather and traveling when dark.

Applications for General Older Adult Population

Mobility affects older adults' perceptions of their environment, and the independence and freedom that is associated with mobility is influential to their well-being (Lawton, 1998). Age-related changes and disabilities experienced by older adults may limit their transportation options, particularly driving. There are approximately 8.4 million adults 65 years and older who do not have a driver's license (Burkhart, McGavock, & Nelson, 2002). There are also older adults who maintain a driver's license and choose to limit their driving or not to drive at all. Many of these older adults who are no longer driving need transportation to work, shopping, medical care, and social activities.

Travel choices are generally limited to depending on family and friends for rides, or public transportation where available. Research shows most older adults prefer not to ask for rides and many are unsure about or uncomfortable with using public transportation. However, research also shows that when given information about how to use public transportation and the opportunity to try the services, people will use them. The National Highway Traffic Safety Administration has identified this issue of mobility and older adults as a compelling problem facing the nation.

Public transportation is a viable solution to this problem, but it is currently underutilized. Public transit accounts for only 3% of trips made by those over age 65 (U.S. Department of Transportation, 1997). The National Health Interview Survey on Disability (1994) found that of older adults 69 and older, there are 28.4% who do not drive and do not use available public transportation.

Reports from focus groups have indicated that older adults do not utilize public transportation for several reasons including availability, accessibility, and apprehensions. There are programs that are targeting the issues of availability and accessibility, but there are few programs addressing the apprehensions of older adults that prohibit them from using public transportation.

In focus groups we have conducted for transportation research, older adults who have never used public transit have reported fears about who rides the bus, getting to the right stop on time, making transfers, and reading maps. Few have attempted to reduce the fears by training older adults how to use the public transportation system. Mobility for older adults would not only increase their independence and well-being but would result in more public transportation passengers.

There is a need for this type of program to increase the mobility for older adults, which is important to both the older adult and to public transit system. One possible solution, building on the travel training model, is for older adults to be trained to use public transportation. Just as older adults are trained to continue driving, they can be trained to deal with the transition from driving to utilizing public transportation. Several approaches to mobility training have been developed and found successful with persons who are intellectually challenged or adults with developmental disabilities. Among those approaches are: orientation and mobility model, educational model, unofficial travel training, customer service model, and companion/familiarity models. These approaches have been successful because they were developed to address the specific needs of the intellectual disabilities/developmental disabilities (ID/DD) population. Although those techniques have been useful for ID/DD populations they will not necessarily be appropriate for older adults because older adults have different needs.

There are very few mobility training programs designed specifically for older adults. Most of those programs recognize the issues relevant to older adults and outline procedures that can be used for training. These programs have integrated principles from the ID/DD training that have been successful (Sterns et al., 1997). To enhance existing training programs for older adults, techniques specific to older adults should be incorporated.

There are several age-related changes that affect older adults' ability to learn. These changes include: sensory changes, slowed information processing, strain on working memory, reduction in inhibitory mechanisms, and limited attentional resources (Salthouse 1991; Schneider, 1997; Hasher & Zacks, 1988). If these changes are addressed, training can be designed to compensate for the changes.

There are two primary ways to address the age-related changes. One way is to change the environment; another way is to change the task. Ways to change the environment include: reducing background noise, providing good lighting to reduce glare, and increasing font size (Charness & Bosman, 1992). Ways to modify the task include: making the task self-paced, breaking the task into its component parts, providing assistance, and allowing time for practice (Belbin & Belbin, 1972; Sterns, 1986).

Not only is it important for older adults to learn the skills needed for public transportation, it is also important that they be able to retain those skills and be able to use the skills in new and different situations. If an older adult doesn't use public transportation for a couple of weeks they need to be able to remember the necessary skills from training. It is also important that an older adult can figure out how to get to the new doctor's office even though they did not practice how to get there. Research shows that distributed practice, the spacing of training, and frequency of feedback can be modified to improve retention (Schmidt & Bjork, 1992).

The effectiveness of mobility training for older adults will be greatly enhanced by addressing issues specific to training older adults. Mobility training is a new approach to an existing problem. Applying training techniques to training older adults to use transportation such as the bus/transit is expected to be successful based on results from existing research. Using well-established training paradigms from special populations, older adults can be trained to identify which type of transportation is most appropriate, read maps, find their way to bus, know when their stop is, understand transfers, acquire necessary aids (e.g., cart for groceries), schedule pick up, or find out time. Supported independence can be obtained for those adults able to remain in the community.

Older adults with intellectual challenges must cope with and utilize the services available to navigate their environment. Other environments can also challenge older adults as they age. A particularly challenging environment to age in is prison. We will examine this unique special population next.

AGING WHILE INCARCERATED
Description of the Population
Prisons are places where the convicted are housed until their release. Traditionally, American prisons have been home to the young and the poor, especially the young male minority offender. Demographic data on the population of prisons since the 1970s suggest that prisons are housing offenders who are quite different from the traditional image. Prisons, reflecting changes in the overall U.S. population, are "graying" (Aday, 2003; Braswell, McCarthy, & McCarthy, 1998). Older inmates are becoming an increasingly important segment of the prison population. States tend to differ in how they implement programs and policies for older prisoners; some recognize the problems with cost and space but have not taken action regarding services to older prisoners. Others have implemented changes to their prison policies for the growing number of older inmates (Aday, 2003). Prisons have become places where many inmates age in place, and where eventually many will die in place.

Recent data suggest that the trend will continue. The incarceration rate for the United States increased from 370 per 100,000 citizens in 1994, to 686 per 100,000 in 2001 (Bureau of Justice Statistics, 2001). This translates to 1 in 146 U.S. residents being incarcerated in a federal or state prison or in a local jail in 2001. In 2008 more than 1 in 100 U.S. adult residents were being incarcerated (Liptak, 2008). State and federal facilities currently number 1,410 (106 are federal institutions). The average daily operating capacity of U.S. adult correctional agencies was 114% (Bureau of Justice Statistics, 2008).

The widespread forecast among states and at the federal level early in this century was that the older inmate population would pose serious challenges for the entire criminal justice system, our communities, and society. This group of inmates (50 years of age and older) is the fastest-growing segment of the U.S. prison population. Over the last two decades, numbers of elderly inmates in American prisons have increased by 750% (Lane, 1999). In 1991, 5.3% of inmates incarcerated in adult correctional agencies were age 50 or older. By 2001, this number increased to 7.9%. The estimated number of prisoners age 55 and older in state and federal prison is just under 80,000 (Bureau of Justice Statistics, 2008). Aday (2003) reports that the number of prisoners aged 50 and over is growing at 10% per year, and that by 2010 the rate of increase will be as high as 20%.

Several changes in the criminal justice system and corrections have contributed to the influx. These include increased length of sentences, mandatory and determinate sentencing, changes in parole granting systems or the elimination of parole, get-tough policies, truth-in-sentencing laws (inmates must serve 85% of terms), and three strikes laws (Braswell et al., 1998; Reiman, 1998). According to Mauer (2002), demand for health care and mental health care services will continue to grow. Clearly, program and policy changes and alternatives designed to cope with aging prisoners need to be explored as this population dramatically increases and ages in place.

Aging of Prisoners Leads to Increasing Costs

Some state, as well as federal, efforts have begun to examine the effects of recent correctional and justice changes on the prison age structure. Some state departments of correction, such as those in Ohio, Pennsylvania, Michigan, Alabama, and North Carolina, have responded by erecting special units or prison blocks to house geriatric inmates. Some of these inmates are in their 80s and 90s. Hocking Correctional Facility (HCF), one of 33 state penal institutions in Ohio, currently houses 474 inmates and has a payroll budget of over $12.7 million per year. In 2002, the average inmate age was 63, with the oldest being 87.5 years (Warden Sam Tambi, personal communication, November 12, 2002). The cost of housing inmates at HCF was over $29,565 per year compared to $23,360 per year average for younger inmates in institutions throughout the state of Ohio. More than half of the Ohio prisons now have older inmate populations greater than 10% (Sterns, Lax, Sed, Keohane, & Sterns 2008).

Over a decade ago, Ohio formed an expert panel to examine options for incorporating more programming and services specific to the needs of the older offenders (including staff development and education initiatives) and for providing community placement options for older inmates upon release (Parks, 1997), and the Ohio Department of Rehabilitation and Corrections continues to push the Ohio legislature for early release programs. Ohio, like Florida and California, needs to free felons from its overcrowded prisons. States are finding it impossible to continue to house young and the more violent inmates along with older prisoners. Many state departments of correction, like Virginia's, are so overcrowded that they sometimes resort to paying neighboring states to incarcerate some of their felons.

Nationally, operating dollars and personnel are being constrained at the same time that medical costs are going up. This is partly due to the increase in older prisoners. The projected cost of housing an elderly inmate nationally is approximately $70,000 per year when infirmity, medical treatments, pharmaceuticals, and hospitalization costs are included (Krane, 1999c; News Journal, 2004). This is compared to the national average across all ages of $22,000 per year. In Ohio, for example, the cost of health care for prisoners is $6.79 per day for those under 50, but is $14.75 per day for those 50 and above (News Journal, 2004). See Table 12.1 for details.

TABLE 12.1
Total Inmate Population: State of Ohio

Fiscal Year	Total PPN[a]	Mean Age[b]
1984	17,340	30.4
1994	40,501	32.7
2002	45,049	34.8

Note. [a]PPN= Total Prison Population/ [b]Mean age in years for selected years.
From Bureau of Research/Office of Policy, Ohio DRC (1996–1999; 2002 reports and fact sheets)

Theories on Aging and Approaches to Service

Older Prisoners Introduce Unique Issues to Corrections

The elderly prison population is composed mainly of three groups. The first entered the correctional system as young offenders and are serving lengthy sentences for violent crimes such as homicides (Kerbs, 2000). The second group is incarcerated using the revolving door. Such inmates are repeat adult offenders, or career criminals, back in prison again for yet another stint. Kerbs (2000) noted that 45.6% of prisoners aged 55 and over are career-criminal recidivists. The third group is composed of those who entered prison for the first time in old age having no prior adult incarcerations. These make up a sizable (41%) proportion of older inmates (Kerbs, 2000). Older inmates, especially those new to the corrections system, have greater vulnerability and feelings of fear for their safety from younger inmates (Aday, 2003).

Health Care Needs

It is clear that younger and older inmates are groups with different prison issues. First, there are clear health differences. Medical care usually increases with age. One estimate suggests that by the year 2005, health care costs for inmates who are older will increase almost 15 times (Vito & Wilson, 1985; Wilson & Vito, 1988). Recently, a survey of 41 states showed a reported rate of 46% chronic physical problems for prisoners over the age of 50 and 82% for prisoners over the age of 65. As the number of prisoners goes from around 17,000 prisoners over 65 in 2008 to over 120,000 in 2022, we can anticipate a 10-fold to 20-fold increase in medical costs (Sterns, Lax, et al., 2008).

Specialized geriatricians and other health professionals with gerontological training are urgently needed to assess the health care needs of the growing numbers of elderly prisoners. They must address such issues as kidney dialysis, glasses, dentures, heart surgery, hypertension, diabetes, AIDS, stroke, cancer, and emphysema. This is a difficult task because in the United States there is currently a shortage of geriatricians and health professionals with training in the unique issues of aging (Frerking, 2000). A recent study of older offenders found that 40% reported arthritis, 39% reported hypertension, and 20% reported the following: ulcers, heart disease, emphysema, and prostate problems (Aday, 2003).

Psychological Needs

The psychological needs of older inmates also differ compared to younger inmates. Differences include how older versus younger inmates handle adjustment to confinement, regulations, and isolation from community and family

(Aday, 2003). Older inmates may feel more hopeless and isolated, become vulnerable to victimization, and grow frail (Dugger, 1988). They may also be less able to cope, feel a greater loss of family and friends, and fear death (Aday, 2003). Depression in older adults may be underdiagnosed because physicians often attribute the symptoms to a physical illness rather than to the aging process. Also, older persons are less likely to complain or to report symptoms (Papalia, Sterns, Feldman, & Camp, 2002). Such underdetection may only compound the need for treatment. Many older inmates have abused drugs and alcohol for many years and suffer from serious mental disorders related to these abuses. Continued and past behaviors may leave the older inmate in poor condition and in need of special treatment services (Krane, 1999b).

Dementia and medical care are especially important issues. Is retribution enough to rationalize continued incarceration if the prisoner no longer knows why he is in prison because he has dementia (Braswell et al., 1998)? Because of the probable increase in medical and mental health costs for the older inmate population, one solution may be to release these older prisoners to the community in order to save the system money (Krane, 1999a). However, older inmates may be more likely to have committed homicide, manslaughter, or serious sexual offenses (Allen & Simonsen, 1998). Some of these inmates have the potential to continue to be violent, and nursing homes are often hesitant to admit such persons.

Education Approaches to Support Service Professionals
There Is a Need for Specialized Training
Mezey, Dubler, Mitty, and Brody (2002) argued that the goals of health, related care, and confinement and punishment may be incompatible. Regardless, it is clear that older inmates differ greatly from their peers and that it is essential for wardens and staff to become knowledgeable about age-related issues. Specialized and preventive care is necessary for elderly inmates, and a failure to provide such care may result in increased health care and litigation costs (Allen & Simonsen, 1998).

Specialized aging training for corrections professionals and staff needs to be designed to provide prison staff with essential gerontological information to facilitate service and program design. This includes information on activities of daily living (ADLs), age-appropriate activities, and alternatives to current housing arrangements in order to alleviate burgeoning correctional budgets and promote institutional safety and security. Having this background is critical for prison staff to be fully involved in the design, delivery, and translation of services to older prisoners.

Examples of Field Successes

As part of an ongoing training project by Sterns, Lax, et al. (2008), a pilot study in 2005 was conducted to explore the awareness among correctional facility staff of issues associated with aging in prison. In qualitative semi-structured interviews wardens, medical officers, and mental health directors across Ohio were asked about problems and issues associated with managing older offenders. Several needs were expressed. The wardens and staff were well aware of the increasing number of older offenders (50 years and older) in prisons. They were also well aware of the issues of managing older inmates and felt that there is a definite need for continuing education and management strategies and policies in this area. Special needs or issues pertaining to this population that were identified include medical care, mobility, safety, education and recreation, mental health, and legal issues.

Medical issues included the costs associated with physical health services, chronic care, dental, disability, and multiple illnesses. Many of these issues overlap. Mobility and sensory declines are tied to safety. There is an awareness that decreased mobility and sensory perception among the older adult inmates creates special needs that must be addressed by correctional facilities to maintain an adequate level of safety. The need for providing age-appropriate education was also identified. At age 70, programming focus should be on continuing education and improving individual level of function in work-related and recreation activities. In terms of the physical structure of the facilities, many were not built to meet the needs of older adults. Recreation was often not age-appropriate, and instead simply focused on activities that are less demanding physically: chair aerobics, shuffleboard, bingo, cards, putt-putt, volleyball, horseshoes, and television viewing.

Preventative Care

In order to control costs, programming must be put in place that keeps older offenders healthy longer, both mentally and physically. Existing programming, activities, and employment opportunities are primarily geared to younger inmates. Another important component is to provide all staff with the knowledge and skills to manage and organize older prisoners. Because older prisoners will make up a growing proportion of the entire prison population, all staff will need some knowledge of aging.

Frontline staff are the key to making preventative health programs a success. Corrections officers must be trained to profile older prisoners. They need a vocabulary of aging to identify and report physical, mental, and social changes so that interventions can be initiated early, when they are inexpensive and short-term.

Perhaps most important are the identification of symptoms of chronic illnesses. These would include heart disease, diabetes, and hepatitis. Sudden changes of any kind, such as changes in weight or appetite, should trigger corrections officers to have older prisoners be seen immediately by health care staff. Immediate concerns are that the problem could result in death, though more likely is that if left untreated, chronic conditions can result in expensive long-term care.

Aging also has an impact on the psychological health of older prisoners. For example, Alzheimer's disease affects 15%–25% of individuals 65 years and older with symptoms beginning in a persons early 60s. Because of the regimented lifestyle of prison, these problems may not be noticed as quickly unless staff are trained to look for specific changes and have a good personal knowledge of the prisoner. Older adults are also more likely to suffer depression that will likely reduce their activity level and social interaction. Because depressed individuals are at risk of suicide, extra awareness on the part of staff can lead to the necessary interventions to return an older inmate to normal. Prevention and awareness can avoid misunderstandings caused by underlying mental health.

Web-based Training Program on Older Prisoner Management and Programming

Through a grant from the National Institutes of Health's National Institute on Aging, Creative Action LLC and Computer Knowledge International have been developing a Web-based training program being implemented for the Ohio Department of Rehabilitation and Corrections. The training focuses on giving frontline officers, health care, and mental health care professionals a comprehensive overview of aging in prison. The training describes biological, psychological, and social aging overlaid in the context of four typical older prisoner types: career criminals, old first-timers, young short-term first timers, and old timers.

The training modules move from reviewing basic aging concepts to describing specific ways to identify physical, mental, and social challenges unique to older inmates. The later modules concentrate on utilizing and understanding ADLs (walking, bending, reaching, lifting, etc.) to best determine if living conditions, employment, and activities are a good fit for older adults. Later modules provide information necessary for staff and professionals to modify existing programs to suit a broader range of abilities for inclusion. The last module is customized for in-house procedures to ensure that officers and professionals know the administrative steps to document and initiate health care and mental health care in their facility to ensure early intervention.

The training modules provide the background necessary to take early action on common and critical chronic conditions and mental health problems. It provides the background necessary to identify situations were activities and housing may be a poor fit with older inmates capabilities. Through the widespread implementation of the training program, Sterns, Lax, et al. (2008) anticipate early identification of problems and better design of activities will slow down the rate of increase in medical costs. With more time, state corrections administrators will have time to modify facilities to better house and provide support services to older inmates. In addition it provides time for administrators to work with state legislators to design programs that allow those who can be released from prison to be provided with aging services in the community were the cost of security can be avoided.

Applications for General Older Adult Population

The application of state-of-art, Web-based training to professionals in work settings dealing with an increasing number of older adults is a robust solution that can be applied in every job setting. Nearly every service sector industry from audiology and banking to yacht sales and zoo tourism will need to deal with the increase in older consumers. Customized training for industries that can be conveniently accessed through the Web, and taken with the flexibility of 24/7 delivery to any shift, is ideal for delivery to the world of business.

There are professionals who need to be trained in aging issues in order to better serve the graying population. But there are also professionals who work with exclusively older populations. But these populations are not static; they are also changing. One particular change is the increase in minorities. With growing numbers of older minority groups, there is the growing challenged of speaking with those older adults who do not speak English well or do not speak English at all. We next discuss the challenges of this special population.

AGING IN THE UNITED STATES WITHOUT SPEAKING ENGLISH

Description of the Population

Many older adults living in long-term care settings speak English as a second language or speak no English at all. Such residents often come from a diversity of ethnic and cultural backgrounds. In our own research we have seen as many as seven different languages spoken by residents in a single facility. Bilingual residents are often reported as returning to the use of their native language in advanced stages of dementia, even if they had not spoken it recently (Yeo, 1993). Delivering comprehensive care to individuals who do not speak English is particularly challenging to the U.S. long-term care industry. Few professionals and low-paid direct care staff have the necessary bilingual skills to provide the same care in a resident's native non-English language as they can deliver in English.

Data from the 1990 U.S. Census indicate that 12% of persons aged 65 and older speak a language other than English, with 47% of these individuals speaking English less than well. Immigration from the former Soviet Union, Eastern Europe, the Far East and Latin America in recent years is likely to substantially increase this number. Many of these older adults will end their lives in care settings such as long-term care (and perhaps in assisted-living) facilities, often while suffering from dementia.

Theories on Aging and Approaches to Service
A Model of Ethnically Sensitive Care of the Elderly

Based on interviews with representatives of six nursing homes identified as Russian Orthodox, Jewish, Japanese, Hispanic, and Asian in Northern California and Washington State, Yeo (1993) developed a model for ethnically sensitive care of the elderly. The model consists of 11 components: (a) Ownership, (B) location, (c) selection and training of staff, (D) admission policy and process, (E) cost, (f) interaction with family, (g) language, (h) food, (i) activities programming, (j) religious observances, and (K) Personal and nursing care (Yeo, 1993). We will use the example of three long-term care facilities that illustrate elements of the model as they serve three ethnic groups: Japanese, Latino, and Russian cultures.

The location of a nursing home plays a key role in whether it is utilized by ethnic populations (Yeo, 1993). The presence of a substantial ethnic community in a city or neighborhood will be reflected in the populations of local nursing homes. For example, in Lorain, Ohio, there is a large population of Hispanic residents, mainly from Puerto Rico, who were drawn to jobs in the steel and auto industries and settled in this Cleveland community. The Hispanic population is well represented at one local nursing home where we completed a research project related to caring for residents who spoke a foreign language.

Ownership by ethnic nonprofit agencies is a key factor behind the development of culturally specific, ethnically sensitive institutions (Yeo, 1993).

This is the case in the example of the Seattle-based Japanese nursing home that was also a part of our study. Members of the Japanese community formed a nonprofit organization in 1976 that owns and operates the Japanese nursing home.

What is unique about these facilities is that environment and caregiving style are sensitive to the needs of residents. This sensitivity extends to observing dietary preferences, providing for ethnically oriented activities, and hosting ethnically appropriate religious observances (Yeo, 1993). The Japanese facility regularly serves traditional Japanese and other Asian dishes such as Korean and Vietnamese style foods. Activity programming reflects the facility's attention to its ethnic and cultural diversity as well. Involvement of family members in the activities and care of residents is also a common factor in ethnically targeted nursing homes (Yeo, 1993).

Ideally, staff with the same ethnicity as the targeted residents are hired. As these facilities are usually found in ethnic neighborhoods, this is often easily accomplished for indirect care staff but not for professionals such as nurses and therapist. Facilities may have difficulty finding and recruiting enough staff from a particular ethnic group (Yeo, 1993). Many administrators turn to training in language, cultural traditions, and ethnic customs to support maintaining a multiethnic, long-term care facility.

Training principally focuses on core cultural and ethnic values and incorporating them into treating residents with dignity and respect (Yeo, 1993). In the two examples discussed earlier, the Japanese- and Hispanic-oriented facilities, efforts to hire ethnic staff have been strong and successful. To provide additional attention and interaction with the residents who speak only a foreign-language, volunteers and family members are recruited to help in the communication with residents. Both of these example facilities have emphasized a measure of training in language and culture for non-Japanese and non-Hispanic staff. Through our research we determined the average non-Spanish-speaking staff member knew 11 words or phrases in Spanish at the Hispanic Facility (Antenucci, Camp, Sterns, Sterns, & Sterns, 2001).

Residents from the local community who happen to be of a different ethnic background are welcomed as new residents even when they are a minority (Yeo, 1993). At a Cleveland-based Orthodox Jewish nursing home, Russian-speaking residents presented communication challenges to staff and residents. The Russian-speaking residents were Jewish, so they had a similar cultural background, but did not speak English, Yiddish, or Hebrew, so communication was challenged.

Similarly, there was a language challenge between new residents from Korea and primarily English- and Japanese-speaking staff at the Japanese facility.

Other Asian ethnic individuals were interested in the food and cultural activities that were ethnically appropriate, but again communication was a central challenge. In a multiethnic long-term care environment, addressing language gaps and increasing communication between staff and residents presents an ongoing challenge.

Examples of Field Successes

Hands-on care staff are trained to explain why they are there and what they are about to do before attempting any care activity with residents. This is particularly important when working with persons with dementia, who may not recognize or remember staff from day to day. Agitated or anxious behavior is less likely when these precautions are taken. When residents do not speak English, and staff members do not speak the language of residents, communication of this type is not possible and providing optimal care impossible.

Sterns and Camp (1998) supported cognitive aging interventions as the key tool for impacting the care of older adults in a substantial way. Interventions can accommodate or compensate for losses in cognitive abilities. No longer being able to speak in a second language that occurs as dementia advances or never speaking the language of the caregiving staff could then be compensated for using an intervention.

In a recent study, Sterns, Sterns, Sterns, and Namazi (2008) proposed a new cognitive intervention program they called the InterpreCare System. The system included a number of elements to provide staff with language to improve the quality of care and the quality of life for residents by overcoming the barrier of language.

Language barriers have existed for some time in long-term care settings, but previous attempts to overcome language barriers have been relatively ineffective. In a Cleveland-based nursing home dealing with Russian-speaking residents, staff were given manuals containing Russian phrases phonetically transcribed into English and placed at the nursing stations in each unit of the facility. No standardized method of training staff was ever implemented. Staff members were not formally trained on how to use the manuals or in pronouncing the Russian phrases. With employee turnover, most staff did not know these manuals existed.

A communication board approach was attempted for the Russian-speaking residents. A list of phrases in the Cyrillic alphabet alongside the English translation of each phrase was printed on a card attached to the resident's walker. Resident's would point to a phrase to communicate. Staff would then look at its corresponding English translation. In another facility, a variation of this approach were slips of paper that were placed in residents' rooms with phrases printed in Cyrillic and corresponding English translations. Unfortunately, this approach did not facilitate staff learning to speak Russian phrases and did not result in the level of interaction and care normally provided. In addition, the intervention was not effective for those residents with visual impairments, severe cognitive impairments, or those who were unable to read.

A third approach seen is to hire bilingual or multilingual staff. In addition to bilingual professionals being rare and requiring a potential premium in salary, when the number of foreign-language-speaking residents is high, this places a burden on individuals who are now required to serve as interpreters, interfering with their ability to perform their own duties. In addition, this does not effectively substitute for the communication required by all staff to conduct delivery of care in a quality manner.

Developed through funding from the National Institute on Aging, the InterpreCare Language System develop by R. Sterns and colleagues (Sterns, Sterns, et al., 2008) bridges the communication gap between English-speaking staff and non-English-speaking residents or patients in health care, social service, and hospitality settings. Currently, systems are available for English-speaking staff to communicate with Russian-, Spanish-, and Japanese-speaking residents, clients, and patients. The InterpreCare System was shown to be successful in enabling English-speaking staff to talk with residents who speak another language. The system is currently in use in over 25 long-term care facilities across the country.

Product Concept and Materials

Throughout their workday, long-term care staff members have opportunities for engaging residents in an exchange of social greetings and dialogue, asking caregiving questions, or requesting residents' cooperation. The InterpreCare System provides an easy way for them to communicate in a foreign language when and where they need to: in the morning in the resident's room, in the afternoon in the dining room, in the evening at the nurse's station. The system provides a way for non-English-speaking residents to communicate in English if they wish. The system includes a video overview and a trainer's manual containing detailed information and instruction designed to prepare the trainer to conduct staff in-services on using the system to communicate with residents in a foreign language.

A self-contained learning station includes audio lessons and materials for practice. The lessons last about 10 minutes and are self-paced and self-monitored. They provide practice with speaking foreign phrases through the use of phonetics (i.e., foreign words and phrases spelled with English letters). Research has shown that with a small amount of practice, staff members begin to feel confident in their ability to speak to residents in a foreign language.

Once the staff have learned to use the phonetic system, there are three elements designed to make use of the phrases easy for staff. These elements include the language boards, in-room boards, and carry cards. The language board is designed for use in a dining room where communication between staff and residents occurs daily. The language board allows staff to view and speak phrases without encumbering their hands while serving, feeding, and giving medication to residents. Color-coding is an important feature of the components. All words and phrases that have to do with meals and food are in a pink color. Green is the color for social greetings. Yellow is reserved for phrases dealing with physical care. Blue is the color used for directives, questions, and general communication phrases.

The in-room board is designed to meet the unique needs of individual residents. In-room boards can be customized with the phrases staff members need to use when working with residents in their rooms. Carry cards are plastic 3" × 5" versions of the language board. These are designed to be easy to clean. A set of cards can be fastened to clothing, kept in a pocket, or attached to a medicine cart. A major benefit of these cards is that they may contain many phrases, not just those used in everyday communication with residents.

For non-English-speaking residents who wish to communicate with English-speaking staff, the InterpreCare System provides a simple way through tabletop boards and resident carry cards. Just as non-English phrases can be spelled phonetically using the English alphabet, English phrases can be spelled using a non-English alphabet. This way, residents do not have to learn another language: they simply speak English words and phrases using the letters and sounds that they already know.

Applications for the General Older Adult Population

While introducing the InterpreCare Language System, the issue of employees with limited proficiency in English arose. From these concerns, the Care Environment English Program was created. We adapted and expanded the products and training concepts of the InterpreCare System to create the Care Environment English (CEE) Program for non-English-speaking staff.

COMMONALITIES IN SPECIAL POPULATIONS

In this chapter we have highlighted some of the challenges of working with special populations, training individuals to work with special populations, and applying techniques for utilizing methods used with special populations in the general aging population. We want to now consider some of the commonalities across the three groups we have specifically discussed here and consider them generally to be applied to other special populations you may encounter or need to incorporate into teaching or research.

Older adults within these subsets are different from their younger counterparts. Older adults with lifelong disabilities are more likely to be in two-generation geriatric contexts. They are less likely to be self-advocates when they require services, medical, or mental health services. They are less likely to have benefited from mainstreaming legislation and early intervention programs that are the normal course of treatment for today's generation of intellectually disabled children.

Older prisoners are different from younger prisoners in their health status, criminal histories, gang involvement, and in their level of ties to the community, friends, and family. Older prisoners entering prison for the first time are significantly disadvantaged in terms of the psychological ability to cope with the stresses of the prison environment.

Elderly non-English speakers are different from their younger counterparts in their devotion to traditions, requirement for culturally specific food, and likelihood of not speaking English well or not speaking English at all.

Each group is likely to wrestle with comorbidities blossoming from midlife onwards. Members of all these groups are disadvantaged and more likely to be poor, and therefore their health care is likely to be significantly less preventative, their diet poorer, and treatment for chronic problems less comprehensive and ongoing. In general, they are going to have more serious health problems and less treatment of mental health problems. Further, each of these groups is in the control of others in terms of access to health care and mental health. So they must have the approval and support of their caregivers in order to receive treatment. At the same time, if they are being well supervised, and housed in a supportive environment with appropriate accommodations, then their care can be delivered more readily and consistently. In their old age there is the potential with proper training and programming to deliver the best care these groups have ever experienced in their lifetimes.

Each group is likely dealing with health issues that affect the learning process and, by implication, the way that subjects are taught to them. For instance, dementia, cognitive impairments, hearing loss, and similar functional impairments are common and affect teaching styles and learning abilities.

Drawing on the experiences of adults with developmental disabilities, Mahon and Mactavish (2000) enumerate practices that activate a sense of belonging or inclusion.

Poe and Edwards (2002) have developed teaching and training techniques that are based on many years of working with adults with intellectual disabilities in group residential and other settings. Their suggestions readily generalize to other groups of would-be employees, students, and clients. Again, Mahon and Mactavish's (2000) principles of belonging are the underlying foundation; the person with age-related or lifelong disabilities is a partner in the learning or service activity, not a passive recipient. Poe and Edwards (2002) have a brief handbook to orient employees who are new to the intellectual disabilities service system. Its recommendations include, and go beyond, the following:

a. Organize learners into small groups, while maintaining a focus on each individual with person-centered planning.
b. Conduct a task analysis—that is, break each desired behavioral or skills outcome into its constituent parts, starting with the most basic task.
c. Explain steps to be learned in concrete rather than abstract terms; even individuals with more involved intellectual disabilities can learn basics that can be built on.
d. Recognize and reward progress; verbal praise is seldom overused.
e. Repeat and practice tasks that have been learned.
f. Employ multimodal instruction techniques (e.g., saying the words of a task while doing the actions).
g. Adjust pacing to the needs of the small group and, further, to the needs of the individuals within that group; at the same time, go beyond the learner's verbal assurance that he or she has acquired what was to be learned.

Persons from special populations, because of their history of powerlessness, particularly those with intellectual disabilities, are often people pleasers. By this we mean that they will say what the questioner wants to hear. Their reliance on others in a supportive environment, their need for assisted autonomy, may condition them to wish to please their helpers, not wanting to let them down. Verify that a task has truly been learned. At the same time, service providers and teachers might themselves benefit from adjusting their own need to push ahead with the next task or the next objective. Communication with individuals with lifelong disabilities has a pace of its own. Everyone involved needs to adjust to its timing, being partners in the process.

Adults from special populations seldom transcend the categorization of care recipient. This status denies them the opportunity to increase their sense of self-worth (and minimize their sense of frustration and impotence thought to underlie some aggression) by helping others and denies others the contributions that these individuals might make (Ansello & Roberto, 1993).

Teaching, training, and services with older adults from special populations can be occasions of mutual growth and learning. Working with these adults can remind us why we became teachers or providers in the first place. Preparing professionals and staff to work with these populations means that you are at the top of pyramid, teaching the information necessary to improve the quality of life for an increasing number of individuals. Each person you teach and each organization they work for will be affected by instilling these better practices and having them implemented. Because of this, we are optimistic about the future, both in terms of the delivery of services to special populations and to the availability of materials to ensure professionals are well trained to deliver those services appropriately.

REFERENCES

Aday, R. (2003). *Aging prisoners' crisis in American corrections.* Westport, CT: Praeger.

Allen, H. E., & C. E. Simonsen. (1998). *Corrections in America* (8th ed.). Upper Saddle River, NJ: Prentice Hall.

Americans with Disabilities Act, 42 U.S.C. §§ 12101-12213 (1990).

Ansello, E. F. (2004). Public policy writ small: Coalitions at the intersection of aging with lifelong disabilities. *Public Policy and Aging Report, 14*(4), 1, 3–6.

Ansello, E. F., & Janicki, M. P. (2000). The aging of nations: Impact on the community, the family, and the individual. In M. P. Janicki & E. F. Ansello (Eds.), *Community supports for aging adults with lifelong disabilities* (pp. 3–18). Baltimore, MD: Paul H. Brookes Publishing.

Ansello, E. F., & Roberto, K. A. (1993). Empowering elderly caregivers: Practice, research, and policy directives. In K. A. Roberto (Ed.), *The elderly caregiver: Caring for adults with developmental disabilities* (pp. 173-189). Thousand Oaks, CA: Sage Publications.

Antenucci, V. M., Camp, C. J., Sterns, H. L. Sterns, R. S., & Sterns A. A. (2001). Overcoming linguistic and cultural barriers: Lessons from long term care settings. In K. H Namazi & P. Chafetz (Eds.), *Assisted living: Current issues in facility management and resident care* (pp. 91–104). Westport, CT: Auburn House.

Belbin, E., & Belbin, R. M. (1972). *Problems in adult retraining.* London: Heinemann.

Braswell, M. C., McCarthy, B. R., & McCarthy, J. B. (1998). *Justice, crime and ethics* (2nd ed.). Cincinnati, OH: Anderson.

Bureau of Justice Statistics. (2001). *Prison statistics.* Retrieved January 16, 2002, from http://www.ojp.usdoj.gov/bjs/prisons.htm

Bureau of Justice Statistics. (2002a). *The number of adults in the correctional population has been increasing.* Retrieved November 13, 2002, from http://www.ojp.usdoj.gov/bjs/glance/corr2.htm

Bureau of Justice Statistics. (2002b). *Over half of the increase in state prison population since 1990.* Retrieved November 13, 2002, from http://www.ojp.usdoj.gov/bjs/glance/corrtyp.htm

Bureau of Justice Statistics. (2008). *Prison statistics.* Retrieved from http://www.ojp.usdoj.gov/bjs/prisons.htm

Burkhart, J. E., McGavock, A. T., & Nelson, C. A. (2002). *Improving transit options for older persons.* Transportation Research Board, Transit Cooperative Research Program B-19. Retrieved October 4, 2008 from http://www.trb.org/TRBNet/ProjectDisplay.asp?ProjectID=1042.

Charness, N., & Bosman, E. A. (1992). Age and human factors. In F. I. M. Craik & T. A. Salthouse (Eds.), *The handbook of aging and cognition* (pp. 495–551). Hillsdale, NJ: Erlbaum.

Developmental Disabilities Assistance and Bill of Rights Act, 42 U.S.C. § 6000 (2000).

Dugger, R. L. (1988). The graying of American prisons: Special care considerations. *Corrections Today, 50,* 26–30, 34.

Education for All Handicapped Children Act. (1975). *Public Law 94-142.* Retrieved October 4, 2008, from http://users.rcn.com/peregrin.enteract/add/94-142.txt

Frerking, B. (2000, February 9). Pool of MDs serving aged is drying up. *The Plain Dealer,* 1A, 7A.

Goldmeier, J., & Herr, S. S. (1999). Empowerment and inclusion in planning. In S. S. Herr & G. Weber (Eds.), *Aging, rights, and quality of life* (pp. 314–326). Baltimore, MD: Paul H. Brookes Publishing.

Hasher, L., & Zacks, R. T. (1988). Working memory, comprehension, and aging: A review and a new view. In G. H. Bower (Ed.), *The psychology of learning and motivation* (Vol. 2, pp. 193–225). San Diego, CA: Academic Press.

Janicki, M. P., & Ansello, E. F. (Eds.). (2000). *Community supports for aging adults with lifelong disabilities.* Baltimore, MD: Paul H. Brookes Publishing.

Kerbs, J. J. (2000) The older prisoner: Social, psychological and medical considerations. In M. B. Rothman, B. D. Dunlop, & P. Entzel (Eds.), *Elders, crime, and the criminal justice system* (pp. 207–228). New York: Springer Publishing.

Krane, J. (April 12, 1999c). *Should elderly convicts be kept in prison?* Retrieved October 25, 2002, from http://www.apbnews.com/cjsystem/behind_bars/oldprisoners/riskcost0412.html

Krane, J. (April 13, 1999b). *Full health coverage for hard criminals.* Retrieved October 25, 2002, from http://www.apbnews.com/cjsystem/behind_bars/oldprisoenrs/health0413.html

Krane, J. (April 13, 1999a). *America's oldest prisoners*. Retrieved October 25, 2002, from http://www.apbnews.com/cjsystem/behind_bars/oldprisoners/oldest 0413.html

LaGrow, S. (1990). Independent travel for developmentally disabled persons: A comprehensive model of instruction. *Research in Developmental Disabilities, 11*(3), 289–301.

Lane, J. (1999, November 4). Graying of prisons balloons by 750%. *The Cleveland Plain Dealer,* 12A.

Laus, M. D. (1977). *Travel instruction for the handicapped.* Springfield, IL: Charles C. Thomas.

Lawton, M. P. (1998). Environment and aging: Theory revisited. In R. J. Scheidt & P. G. Windley (Eds.), *Environment and aging theory. A focus on housing* (pp. 1–31). Westport, CT: Greenwood Press.

Liptak, A. (2008). Inmate count in U.S. dwarfs other nation's: Tough laws and long terms create gap. *The New York Times National, 157,* A1–A14.

Mahon, M. J., & Mactavish, J. B. (2000). A sense of belonging: Older adults' perspectives on social integration. In M. P. Janicki & E. F. Ansello (Eds.), *Community supports for aging adults with lifelong disabilities* (pp. 41–54). Baltimore, MD: Paul H. Brookes Publishing.

Mauer, M. (2002). Analyzing and responding to the driving forces of prison population growth. *Criminology and Public Policy, 1*(3), 389–392.

Mezey, M., Dubler, N. N., Mitty, E., & Brody, A. A. (2002). What impact do setting and transitions have on the quality of life at the end of life and the quality of the dying process? *The Gerontologist, 42*(3), 54– 67.

Moody, H. R. (1992). *Ethics in an aging society.* Baltimore, MD: The Johns Hopkins University Press.

National Health Interview Survey on Disability. (1998). *Phase 1 and Phase 2, 1995* [machine-readable data file and documentation, CD-ROM Series 10, No 10A]. Hyattsville, MD: National Center for Health Statistics.

Ohio Department of Rehabilitation and Correction. (2001). *FY 2001 annual report.* Retrieved November 12, 2002, from http://www.drc.state.oh.us

Ohio Department of Rehabilitation and Correction. (2002). *Fact sheets.* Retrieved November 12, 2002, from http://www.drc.state.oh.us/web/october02(November02).pdf

Papalia, D. E., Sterns, H. L., Feldman, R. D., & Camp, C. J. (2002). *Adult development and aging* (2nd ed.). Boston: McGraw Hill.

Parks, E. (1997). *Older offenders: The Ohio initiative.* Columbus, OH: Ohio Department of Rehabilitation and Correction.

Poe, L., & Edwards, G. (2002). *Mental retardation staff orientation workbook* (revised November 2002). Richmond, VA: Office of Mental Retardation, Virginia Department of Mental Health, Mental Retardation and Substance Abuse Services.

Reiman, J. (1998). *The rich get richer and the poor get prison* (5th ed.). Boston: Allyn and Bacon.

Rehabilitation Research and Training Center. (2008). *The Rehabilitation Research and Training Center on Aging and Developmental Disabilities.* Retrieved July 28, 2008, from http://www.uic.edu/orgs/rrtcamR/index.html

Salthouse, T. A. (1991). *Theoretical perspectives on cognitive aging.* Hillsdale, NJ: Lawrence Erlbaum Associates.

Schalock, R. L., & Luckasson, R. (2004). American Association on Mental Retardation's definition, classification, and system of supports and its relation to international trends and issues in the field of intellectual disabilities. *Journal of Policy and Practice in Intellectual Disabilities, 1*(3/4), 136–146.

Schmidt, R. A., & Bjork, R. A. (1992). New conceptualizations of practice: Common principles in three paradigms suggest new concepts for training. *Psychological Science, 3*(4), 207–217.

Schneider, B. A. (1997). Psychoacoustics and aging: Implications for everyday listening. *Journal of Speech-Language Pathology and Audiology, 21,* 111–124.

Sterns, H. L. (1986). Training and retraining adult and older adult workers. In J. E. Birren, P. K. Robinson, & J. E. Livingston (Eds.), *Age, health, and employment* (pp. 93–113). Englewood Cliffs, NJ: Prentice-Hall.

Sterns, H. L., & Camp, C. J. (1998). Applied gerontology. *Applied Psychology: An International Review, 47,* 175–198.

Sterns, A. A., Lax, G., Sed, C., Keohane, P., & Sterns, R.S. (2008). The growing wave of older prisoners: A national survey of older prisoner health, mental health, and programming. *Corrections Today, 70,* 70–76.

Sterns, A. A., Mattern, J., Sterns, R. S., & Wright-Penov, C. (2003). *Validating assessment and travel training instruction.* Washington, DC: Project ACTION.

Sterns, R. S., Nelson, C. A., Sterns, H. L., Fleming, J. C., Brigati, P., McLary, J., & Stahl, A. (1997). *Public transportation in an aging society: The potential role of service routes.* Washington, DC: AARP.

Sterns, H. L., Sterns, R. S., Sterns, A. A., & Namazi (2007, November). *The InterpreCare System.* Presentation for 60th Annual Scientific Meeting Gerontological Sciety of America. San Francisco, California.

Suen, S. L., & Mitchell, C. G. B. (1993). *Accessible transportation and mobility (TR 1378).* Washington, DC: Transportation Research Board.

Tobias, J. (1963). *Training for independent living.* New York: Association for Help of Retarded Children.

U.S. Department of Transportation (1997). *Improving Transportation for a Maturing Society,* DOT-P10-07-01, Office of the Assistant Secretary for Transportation Policy, Washington, DC.

U.S. Rehabilitation Act, 29 U.S.C. § 791-794 (1973).

Vito, G. F., & Wilson, D. G. (1985). Forgotten people: Elderly inmates. *Federal Probation, 49,* 18–24.

Wilson, D. G., & Vito, G. F. (1988). Long-term inmates: Special need and management considerations. *Federal Probation, 52,* 21–26.

Wolfensberger, W. (1972). *The principle of normalization in the human services.* Toronto: National Institute of Mental Retardation.

Yeo, G. (1993). Ethnicity and nursing homes: Factors affecting use and successful components for culturally sensitive care. In C. M. Barresi & D. E. Stull (Eds.), *Ethnic elderly and long-term care* (pp. 161–177). New York: Springer Publishing.

Index

224   Index